FRED TONEY

D0913188

INTRODUCTION TO
MODERN ALGEBRAIC CONCEPTS

INTRODUCTION TO
MODERN ALGEBRAIC CONCEPTS

MAX D. LARSEN
University of Nebraska

ADDISON-WESLEY PUBLISHING COMPANY
Reading, Massachusetts · Menlo Park, California · London · Don Mills, Ontario

This book is in the
ADDISON-WESLEY SERIES IN
INTRODUCTORY MATHEMATICS

Consulting Editors
Richard S. Pieters
Gail S. Young

To my wife Lillie

PREFACE

This book was written to be a text for a first course in modern abstract algebra. It grew out of notes prepared for the courses I taught at the University of Kansas and at the University of Nebraska from 1965 to 1968. It has been used in courses for undergraduate mathematics majors, in courses for prospective secondary school mathematics teachers, and in courses for combinations of these two groups. The materials presented were chosen in such a way as to introduce both these groups to modern abstract algebra.

The basic objectives of the book are three. First of all, the book is meant to introduce the student to the terminology, concepts, and methods of modern abstract algebra. Next, the student must be acquainted with the notion of proof—to be able to recognize and understand a proof and to be able to construct proofs himself. Finally, the student must be cognizant of the general procedure for developing the theory of an algebraic system from the axioms of that system.

Except for a few examples, no previous knowledge of modern algebra is required. We assume only that the reader knows what the integers are—in other words we assume only that he can count. The most important ingredient needed from the student is a desire to learn and a willingness to work. When certain well-known facts about the integers are needed, they will be assumed as axioms and then proved (independently) in Chapter 7.

Chapter 1 contains various fundamental concepts necessary for understanding the remainder of the material in the book—sets, mappings, equivalence relations, and binary operations. A short section on symbolic logic is also included. This section, along with a section on mathematical induction, is meant to form a basis for writing proofs. Because of its frequent use in the sequel, the division algorithm for the integers is given here also. For many students, this chapter is unnecessary except possibly for review or for establishing common notation. However, for other students, these concepts must be considered carefully.

I have treated groups before rings in this book. It has been my experience that students grasp abstractions much more easily if they are indeed abstract rather than "almost abstract." By this I refer to the approach to abstract algebra which commonly treats rings first as an abstraction of the integers. In line with my philosophy here, I have tended to hold detailed examples until some rudimentary grasp of the abstract system has been established. Chapter 2 on groups is followed by Chapter 3 on rings.

In the fourth chapter, the ring of integers and its properties of divisibility are considered. The exercises here provide practice for the student in writing proofs in a system with which he is more familiar than he is with the groups and rings of the previous chapters. This chapter provides a nice change of pace.

Chapter 5 deals with integral domains and fields. In particular this chapter deals with two important concepts—ordered integral domains and fields and the field of quotients of an integral domain. This chapter also contains specific results concerning the field of rational numbers.

Polynomials are constructed in Chapter 6, and their divisibility properties are studied by referring to the same properties for the integers. Irreducibility of polynomials over given fields—in particular, the rational field—is given special attention.

In Chapter 7 a development of the real number system is outlined. Many of the details here are left to the student as exercises. However, after completing the majority of the preceding material, the student should not find the going too tough!

The exercises are a vital part of the book. Only through the exercises will the students learn the concepts involved. Many exercises are used in subsequent proofs, and many proofs are left to the student as exercises. To consider the course complete, each student must complete these exercises.

Each definition and theorem is numbered; the first number indicates the chapter, the second the section, and the third its position in the section. Additional references are given at the end of each chapter.

I have left to the teacher the responsibility of pointing out the relationships between the various algebraic systems. The student should be aware of the fact that we have progressed from simple to complex—from groups to fields—by adding new axioms.

I wish to thank all the people who assisted in the preparation of this book. It is impossible to list all those to whom I am indebted. Any work I do in mathematics is influenced by my teacher, Paul J. McCarthy, who made modern algebra fascinating to me. I would like to thank my colleagues for their many helpful suggestions, and especially I wish to thank Professor Edwin Halfar for his many kind and patient discussions with me while I was preparing the manuscript. I am indebted to Richard Shumway for reading the manuscript and for his valuable suggestions and to Mike Alt for urging me to write the book in the beginning.

Lincoln, Nebraska   M. D. L.
September, 1968

NOTE TO THE STUDENT

For many of you, this course will be your first encounter with abstract mathematics. Consequently, a word concerning your approach to the concepts presented in this book may be worthwhile. If you are dealing with mathematics from an abstract point of view for the first time, you will no doubt find it quite different from the other courses you have had in mathematics, such as calculus and differential equations. Many students of mathematics, as well as many professional mathematicians, find the purity of an abstract approach quite refreshing. I certainly do and I sincerely hope you can experience some of the excitement and joy that I find in mathematics.

The only requirement made of you is that you have an alert and creative mind and that you *work*. Except in extreme cases, the material presented here will remain dead for you unless you are able through your own work and participation in the course to bring life to these exciting concepts. You are past the stage in your mathematical training in which it is sufficient to memorize a formula and apply it to various problems. Now you must *think*, and for many of us that means *work*.

A majority of the activities asked of a student studying abstract algebra consists of writing proofs of the various theorems. For many of you this will be a new experience. In general, there is no prescribed or established pattern to follow in writing proofs. Mark my words, you will soon be complaining, "I do not know how to get started writing the proof." There is no answer to your dilemma except to try every way you can think of until you find one that works. By a careful consideration of the facts you know, the hypothesis of the theorem you are trying to prove, and the conclusion for which you are striving, you should be able to ferret out the essential points and thus have a basis from which to "get started." If you try one approach and it does not seem to work, abandon it and try another. Do not give up simply because the first attempt fails. As you gain experience, your first approach will fail less often. This "experience" to which I refer comes from working on proofs until you succeed in writing a correct proof even though you may make several false starts.

Your next question will probably be "How do I know my proof is correct?" The fact that this question has an easy answer is one major reason for the appeal of abstract mathematics. Every system of mathematics is based on certain logical principles, on undefined terms and definitions based on them, and on certain axioms. If at every step of your proof you comply with the rules of logic and with the definitions and axioms of your system, then your proof will be correct. Hence the validity of a proof depends solely upon the validity of each individual step.

With a concentration on proving each theorem, there is a danger of "missing the forest because of all the trees." One aspect of the treatment of modern algebra in this book that must not be missed is the method one employs in investigating an algebraic system. There are certain questions that one usually asks concerning the properties of an algebraic system which aid in the development of the theory associated with the system. You must be aware of these questions. At the conclusion of your work with algebraic systems in this book, you should be able to begin with the definitions and axioms of a completely new system and develop the properties of it.

Let me close this note with an anecdote which sums up what I have been saying. At the beginning of each semester of classes at the University of Kansas, Professor G. Baley Price, the chairman of the mathematics department, has a meeting of all staff members. At this meeting, he reminds all that are present—graduate teaching assistants and professors alike—of a statement attributed to Professor John L. Kelley: "Mathematics is not a spectator sport." The wisdom in these words becomes more evident the longer one studies mathematics. If you have an honest interest in mathematics, then get out of the grandstand and get to *work*! The world of mathematics is yours if you are willing to be one of the "players."

M. D. L.

CONTENTS

Chapter 1   Fundamental Concepts

1.1   Sets 1
1.2   Mappings 4
1.3   Logic and Methods of Proof 9
1.4   Equivalence Relations 16
1.5   Binary Operations 19
1.6   Division Algorithm for the Integers 20
1.7   Mathematical Induction 21

Chapter 2   Groups

2.1   Definition of a Group 24
2.2   Simple Properties of Groups 26
2.3   Examples of Groups 30
2.4   Subgroups 38
2.5   Cosets and Langrange's Theorem 43
2.6   Normal Subgroups and Factor Groups 46
2.7   Homomorphisms and Isomorphisms 52

Chapter 3   Rings

3.1   Definition of a Ring 57
3.2   Simple Properties of a Ring 59
3.3   Examples of Rings 62
3.4   Generalized Sums and Products 67
3.5   Subrings and Ideals 70
3.6   Homomorphisms 73

Chapter 4   The Integers

4.1   Divisibility and Primes 77
4.2   Greatest Common Divisor 80
4.3   The Fundamental Theorem of Arithmetic 85

Chapter 5   Integral Domains and Fields

5.1   Definitions 88
5.2   Simple Properties 90

5.3   The Field of Quotients of an Integral Domain   92
5.4   Ordered Integral Domains   97
5.5   The Field of Rational Numbers   99

Chapter 6   Polynomials

6.1   Definition of Polynomials   103
6.2   Divisibility and the Division Algorithm   110
6.3   Greatest Common Divisor and Unique Factorization   . . . 115
6.4   Polynomials Over the Field of Rational Numbers   117
6.5   The Ring of Polynomials Modulo $f(x)$ 120

Chapter 7   The Real Number System

7.1   The Natural Numbers   123
7.2   The Integers   126
7.3   The Real Numbers   128
7.4   The Complex Numbers   134

CHAPTER 1

FUNDAMENTAL CONCEPTS

1.1 SETS

The terms *set* and *element of a set* are undefined terms, just as point and line are undefined terms in geometry. The word "set" is synonymous with collection. Each set is associated with certain other objects called *elements*, which are said to be *members of the set*. We usually denote sets by capital Latin letters and elements by lower case Latin letters. Suppose A is a set and x is an element of A. We denote this relationship symbolically by $x \in A$. The statement $x \in A$ is read "x is a member of A," "x belongs to A," or "x is in A." Observe that the symbol $\in$ must have a set on the right and an element on the left. If y is an element which is not a member of B, we write $y \notin B$. For instance, if I denotes the set of all integers, then $3 \in I$ and $\frac{1}{3} \notin I$.

A set may be specified in two ways. First, the elements of the set may be listed within braces; e.g., $C = \{a, b, c, d\}$ is a set having exactly four members: $a, b, c,$ and d. Moreover, if Q is the set of positive integers larger than 9, we can write $Q = \{10, 11, 12, 13, \ldots\}$ where ... means "and so on." An alternative method of specifying a set is to describe the elements of the set by listing their properties. For instance, the Q statement above could have been written $Q = \{x \mid x \text{ is a positive integer and } x > 9\}$. Moreover, if P is the set of positive integers, then $Q = \{x \mid x \in P \text{ and } x > 9\}$. One reads this expression "Q is the set of all x such that $x \in P$ and $x > 9$."

We will say a set A is a *subset* of a set B if every member of A is also a member of B. We denote the fact that A is a subset of B by $A \subseteq B$ and often say "A is contained in B." Note that every set is a subset of itself. The set which has no members is called the *empty* (or *null*) set and is denoted by $\emptyset$. Note that for any set A, $\emptyset \subseteq A$. If A is a nonempty set which is a subset of a set B, and if B contains an element which is not a member of A, then A is said to be a *proper* subset of B; we denote this by $A \subset B$. The symbols $\subseteq$ and $\subset$ are used to show a relationship between two sets and not between an element and a set. With one exception, if a is a member of a set A, we may write $a \in A$ or $\{a\} \subseteq A$, but not $a \subseteq A$. The exception is $\emptyset \in \{\emptyset\}$ and $\emptyset \subseteq \{\emptyset\}$. We say two sets A and B are *equal* and write $A = B$ if $A \subseteq B$ and $B \subseteq A$; i.e., $A = B$ if and only if A is a subset of B and B is a subset of A. Thus, to prove that two sets A and B are equal, it suffices to prove that

1

every member of A is also a member of B and that every member of B is also a member of A.

There are two operations that combine two sets. The *intersection* of the two sets A and B, written $A \cap B$, is the set $\{x \mid x \in A \text{ and } x \in B\}$. Hence the intersection of the sets A and B is the set of all elements which are both in A and in B. Consider the following examples. For any set A, $A \cap A = A$. Whenever $A \subseteq B$ for any sets A and B, $A \cap B = A$. If $A = \{1, 2, 3, 4\}$ and $B = \{3, 4, 5\}$, then $A \cap B = \{3, 4\}$. If A is the set of all coeds and B is the set of all mathematics majors, then $A \cap B$ is the set of all coeds majoring in mathematics. Pictorially, the intersection of two sets A and B can be represented by a *Venn diagram* (Fig. 1.1). Here A is the circle on the left, B is the circle on the right, and $A \cap B$ is the shaded part. If two sets A and B have no elements in common, then their intersection $A \cap B$ is the empty set $\emptyset$. In this case, we say that A and B are *disjoint*.

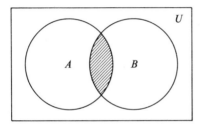
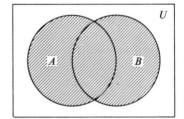

Figure 1.1   Figure 1.2

A second operation used to combine two sets is the *union* of two sets. The union of two sets A and B, written $A \cup B$, is the set $\{x \mid x \in A \text{ or } x \in B\}$; i.e., the union of two sets A and B is the set of all x such that x belongs to A, to B, or to both. Let us look at examples analogous to those considered above. For any set A, $A \cup A = A$. If $A \subseteq B$ for any two sets A and B, then $A \cup B = B$. If $A = \{1, 2, 3, 4\}$ and $B = \{3, 4, 5\}$, then $A \cup B = \{1, 2, 3, 4, 5\}$. If A is the set of all university women and B is the set of all mathematics majors, then $A \cup B$ is the set of all university students who are either women or mathematics majors or both. The union of two sets A and B can be illustrated pictorially as in Fig. 1.2, where A is the circle on the left, B is the circle on the right, and $A \cup B$ is the shaded part.

It is easy to extend the concepts of intersection and union of two sets to the intersection and union of a finite number of sets. For instance, if $X_1, X_2, \ldots, X_n$ are sets, then

$$X_1 \cap X_2 \cap \cdots \cap X_n = \{x \mid x \in X_i \text{ for all } i = 1, 2, \ldots, n\}$$

and

$$X_1 \cup X_2 \cup \cdots \cup X_n = \{x \mid x \in X_i \text{ for some } i = 1, 2, \ldots, n\};$$

i.e., the intersection of the sets $X_1, X_2, \ldots, X_n$ is the set of elements which belong to all of the X_i ($1 \leq i \leq n$), and the union of the sets $X_1, X_2, \ldots, X_n$ is the set of elements which belong to at least one of the X_i ($1 \leq i \leq n$).

Let U be a given set. If $X_1, X_2, \ldots, X_n$ are all subsets of U such that

$$U = X_1 \cup X_2 \cup \cdots X_n$$

and

$$X_i \cap X_j = \emptyset \qquad \text{for all } i, j, i \neq j,$$

then we say $X_1, X_2, \ldots, X_n$ form a *partition* of U. Thus, if $X_1, X_2, \ldots, X_n$ form a partition of U, then every element of U belongs to one of the X_i's, but no element of U belongs to more than one of the X_i's. A partition of a set U divides U into disjoint subsets such that each member of U belongs to exactly one of the subsets. For instance, the sets $\{1, 5\}$, $\{2, 3, 6\}$, $\{7\}$, $\{4, 8, 9\}$ form a partition of the set $\{1, 2, 3, 4, 5, 6, 7, 8, 9\}$.

If A and B are sets, we define the *Cartesian product $A \times B$* of A and B to be the set of all ordered pairs (a, b) where $a \in A$ and $b \in B$; i.e.,

$$A \times B = \{(a, b) \mid a \in A, b \in B\}.$$

If $a, c \in A$ and $b, d \in B$, then we define *equals* by $(a, b) = (c, d)$ if and only if $a = c$ and $b = d$. For $A = \{1, 2\}$ and $B = \{x, y, z\}$, $A \times B = \{(1, x),$ $(1, y), (1, z), (2, x), (2, y), (2, z)\}$. The concept of the Cartesian product of two sets can be extended to the Cartesian product of a finite number of sets. The Cartesian product of the sets $X_1, X_2, \ldots, X_n$ is

$$X_1 \times X_2 \times \cdots \times X_n = \{(x_1, x_2, \ldots, x_n) \mid x_i \in X_i \text{ for } i = 1, 2, \ldots, n\};$$

that is, $X_1 \times X_2 \times \cdots \times X_n$ is the set of all n-tuples $(x_1, x_2, \ldots, x_n)$ where the ith entry is from X_i.

1.1.1 Exercises

1. Given that $A = \{0, 2, 4, 6\}$, $B = \{1, 4, 5, 6, 7\}$, $C = \{1, 3, 5, 8\}$, and $D = \emptyset$, compute the following.

   a) $A \cup B$ b) $B \cap C$ c) $B \cup C$
   d) $A \cap C$ e) $A \cap D$ f) $C \cup D$
   g) $(A \cap B) \cup C$ h) $(B \cup C) \cap A$ i) $A \times B$

2. Observe that the expression $A \cap B \cup C$ is meaningless. Should one find the intersection of A and B and then compute the union of $A \cap B$ and C; or should one find the union of B and C first and then compute the intersection of A and $B \cup C$? The first procedure could be expressed by $(A \cap B) \cup C$; the second by $A \cap (B \cup C)$. Find examples of sets A, B, and C which show that $(A \cap B) \cup C$ and $A \cap (B \cup C)$ are not identical.

3. If U is a set and A is a subset of U, $\bar{A}$ will denote the set of all elements in U which are not in A. Then $\bar{A}$ is called the *complement of A in U*.

Let $U = \{a, b, c, d, e, f, g, h, i\}$, $A = \{a, b, c, d\}$, $B = \{c, d, e\}$, and $C = \{e, h, i\}$. Compute the following sets.

a) $\tilde{A}$ b) $\tilde{A} \cap \tilde{B}$ c) $\widetilde{(A \cup B)}$

d) $\widetilde{(A \cap B)} \cap C$ e) $\tilde{\tilde{A}}$ f) $\widetilde{(A \cap B)} \cup C$

g) $(A \cap B) \cup \tilde{C}$ h) $A \cap \tilde{A}$ i) $B \cup \tilde{B}$

4. Give three different partitions of the set of positive integers.

5. Does $A \times (B \cup C) = (A \times B) \cup (A \times C)$? What about $A \cap (B \times C) = (A \cap B) \times (A \cap C)$? Prove your answers.

6. Prove that $A \cap B = B \cap A$ and $A \cup B = B \cup A$, but that $A \times B \neq B \times A$.

1.2 MAPPINGS

We will first consider an example. Let C be the set of pages in this book, and let P be the set of positive integers. Then, by numbering the pages, we are associating with each element of C a certain number, an element of P. This is an example of a mapping from the set C to the set P. Other examples will follow. Right now let us give a precise definition of mapping.

*1.2.1 Definition. A **mapping** α from a set A to a set B is a correspondence that associates with each element a of A a unique element b of B. We denote this correspondence by writing $\alpha(a) = b$ and we call b the **image of** a **under** α.*

Two shorthand methods of indicating that α is a mapping from a set A to a set B are $\alpha: A \to B$ and $A \xrightarrow{\alpha} B$. It is important to observe that "mapping" is simply another word for "function." Most readers are familiar with functions from calculus. The two terms are identical. "Mapping" is most commonly used in algebra, "function" in connection with analysis.

There are two words in the definition of mapping that merit examination. One is "each"; in order that α be a mapping defined on the set A, α must be defined for all elements of A. Thus, for each $a \in A$, $\alpha(a)$ is some element of B. The second word deserving extra emphasis is "unique." For each $a \in A$, there is only one associated element of B; that is, for each $a \in A$, $\alpha(a)$ can be only one element of B. A correspondence which satisfies this "uniqueness" is said to be *well defined*.

We must ask ourselves what is meant when one says that two mappings are *equal*. For two mappings α and β to be equal, they must first be defined on the same set. In addition, the image under α and that under β must be the same for each element of the set on which they are defined. Thus two mappings α and β defined on the same set A are *equal* if $\alpha(a) = \beta(a)$ for each $a \in A$.

1.2.2 Examples

1. Let $A = \{1, 2, 3, 4\}$ and $B = \{u, v, w\}$. Then the correspondence

$$\alpha(1) = u, \qquad \alpha(2) = v, \qquad \alpha(3) = v, \qquad \alpha(4) = w$$

is a mapping from A to B. Note that the fact that 2 and 3 have the same image under α does not contradict the "uniqueness" required in the definition of mapping. The elements 2 and 3 each have unique images; it simply happens that they both have the same image. But neither of them has more than one image, so α is a mapping.

2. Let A be any set. The correspondence which associates each element of A with itself is clearly a mapping from A to A. We denote this mapping by ι (iota) and call it the *identity mapping* on A. Then $\iota(a) = a$ for all $a \in A$.

3. Let I be the set of all integers, and define a correspondence β from I to itself by $\beta(i) = i + 1$ for all $i \in I$. To see that β is a mapping, one must show that for each $i \in I$, $i + 1$ is an element of I and that for each $i \in I$, there is only one element of the form $i + 1$ in I. It is easy to see that both these conditions hold. Thus β is a mapping.

4. Let I be the set of all integers, and define a correspondence ρ from I to itself by $\rho(x) = x^2 - x$ for all $x \in I$. Then ρ is a mapping. (Check it!)

One can illustrate the definition of a mapping α from a set A to a set B as in Fig. 1.3.

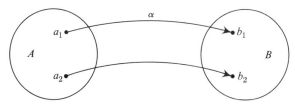

Figure 1.3

Here the circle on the left denotes A and the one on the right, B. The arrows go from elements of A to their images in B. Thus, for α to be a mapping, each element of A must be the initial point of an arrow, and no point of A can be the initial point of two arrows. The mapping α in Example 1.1 above is shown in Fig. 1.4.

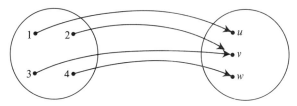

Figure 1.4

1.2.3 Definition. *A mapping α from a set A to a set B is said to be a mapping of A **onto** B if every element of B is the image of some element of A.*

Thus, if α is a mapping of A *onto* B, then for each $b \in B$, there exists an element $a \in A$ such that $\alpha(a) = b$. In the pictorial illustration of a mapping (Fig. 1.4), a mapping $\alpha: A \to B$ would be *onto* B if every element of B was the tip of some arrow. The mapping α in Example (1) is *onto*, since each of of the elements u, v, and w of B are images of some element of A. The identity mapping ι is clearly onto. The mapping β of Example (3) is a mapping from I onto I, since, given any i in I, it is the image of the element $i - 1 \in I$ since $\beta(i - 1) = (i - 1) + 1 = i$. However, the mapping ρ of Example (4) is *not onto* since the element $3 \in I$ is not the image of any $x \in I$.

1.2.4 Definition. *A mapping α from a set A to a set B is said to be **one-to-one** if distinct elements of A have distinct images in B.* (Two elements are distinct if they are unequal.)

Thus, if α is a *one-to-one* mapping from a set A to a set B, then for all elements $a_1, a_2 \in A$ such that $a_1 \neq a_2$, we must have $\alpha(a_1) \neq \alpha(a_2)$. An equivalent way to express this is: α is *one-to-one* if, for a_1, $a_2 \in A$, $\alpha(a_1) = \alpha(a_2)$ implies $a_1 = a_2$. Pictorially a mapping is *one-to-one* if no two arrows have the same tip. The mapping α in Example (1) is not *one-to-one* since 2 and 3 have the same image; i.e., $\alpha(2) = \alpha(3)$, but $2 \neq 3$. The identity mapping ι is clearly *one-to-one*. The mapping β of Example (3) is *one-to-one*; for, if $i, j \in I$ and $i \neq j$, then $i + 1 \neq j + 1$. Hence $i \neq j$ implies $\beta(i) \neq \beta(j)$. In Example (4), ρ is not *one-to-one* since $\rho(0) = \rho(1)$ but $0 \neq 1$. (Check!)

To summarize, Example (1) shows a mapping which is onto but not one-to-one; Example (3), one which is onto and one-to-one; Example (4), one which is neither onto nor one-to-one. We leave it as an exercise to find an example of a mapping which is one-to-one, but not onto. Thus one can see that the concepts of *onto* mappings and *one-to-one* mappings are completely independent.

Consider the following situation: Let A, B, and C be sets, let α be a mapping from A to B, and let β be a mapping from B to C. Let a be an element of A. Then $\alpha(a)$ is an element of B, and consequently it makes sense to ask, "What is the image of $\alpha(a)$ under β?" It would be $\beta(\alpha(a))$; i.e., β of $\alpha(a)$. In this way, for each element a of A, we can associate an element of C —namely $\beta(\alpha(a))$. Thus α and β can be combined to produce a mapping from A to C. This is the basis of the following definition.

1.2.5 Definition. *If A, B, and C are sets and $\alpha: A \to B$ and $\beta: B \to C$, then the **composition of α and β** is the mapping $\beta \circ \alpha: A \to C$ defined by $(\beta \circ \alpha)(a) = \beta(\alpha(a))$ for all $a \in A$.*

Thus, in the situation in this definition, $(\beta \circ \alpha)(a)$ will mean one first applies α to a, and then one applies β to $\alpha(a)$. *Note* that, in order for the composition $\sigma \circ \rho$ of two mappings σ and ρ to make sense, ρ must have its images in the set on which σ is defined.

Let us illustrate the composition of two mappings by some examples.

1.2.6 Examples

1. Let $A = \{1, 2, 3, 4\}$, $B = \{u, v, w\}$, and $C = \{a, b, c\}$. Define $\alpha: A \to B$ and $\beta: B \to C$ by

$$\alpha(1) = u, \qquad \alpha(2) = v, \qquad \alpha(3) = v, \qquad \alpha(4) = w$$

and

$$\beta(u) = a, \qquad \beta(v) = b, \qquad \beta(w) = b.$$

Let us compute the composition $\beta \circ \alpha$. The element $(\beta \circ \alpha)(1)$ is, by definition, the application of α to 1 and then β to the result. Thus

$$(\beta \circ \alpha)(1) = \beta\big(\alpha(1)\big) = \beta(u) = a.$$

Thus $(\beta \circ \alpha)(1) = a$. Similarly $(\beta \circ \alpha)(2) = \beta\big(\alpha(2)\big) = \beta(v) = b$, $(\beta \circ \alpha)(3) = \beta\big(\alpha(3)\big) = \beta(v) = b$, and $(\beta \circ \alpha)(4) = \beta\big(\alpha(4)\big) = \beta(w) = b$. Consequently,

$$(\beta \circ \alpha)(1) = a, \qquad (\beta \circ \alpha)(2) = b, \qquad (\beta \circ \alpha)(3) = b, \qquad (\beta \circ \alpha)(4) = b.$$

In this case, $\alpha \circ \beta$ does not make sense.

2. Let A be any set, and let ι be the identity mapping on A. If α is any other mapping from A to itself, then $\alpha \circ \iota = \iota \circ \alpha = \alpha$. To see this, let $a \in A$, and observe that $(\alpha \circ \iota)(a) = \alpha\big(\iota(a)\big) = \alpha(a)$ and $(\iota \circ \alpha)(a) = \iota\big(\alpha(a)\big) = \alpha(a)$.

3. Let I be the set of all integers, and let β and ρ be the mappings defined in Examples (3) and (4) of 1.2.2; i.e., $\beta: I \to I$ is defined by $\beta(i) = i + 1$ for all $i \in I$, and $\rho: I \to I$ is defined by $\rho(i) = i^2 + i$ for all $i \in I$. Then $\rho \circ \beta$ and $\beta \circ \rho$ both make sense. Furthermore,

$$(\rho \circ \beta)(i) = \rho\big(\beta(i)\big) = \rho(i + 1) = (i + 1)^2 + i + 1 = i^2 + 3i + 2$$

for all $i \in I$ and

$$(\beta \circ \rho)(i) = \beta\big(\rho(i)\big) = \beta(i^2 + i) = (i^2 + i) + 1 = i^2 + i + 1.$$

Hence we see that even if $\rho \circ \beta$ and $\beta \circ \rho$ are both sensible, they may not be the same mapping.

Next we state and prove a lemma (associative law) which relates an important property of the composition of mappings—namely, when the necessary compositions make sense, the composition of mappings is associative.

1.2.7 Lemma. *If A, B, C, and D are sets, and if $\alpha: A \to B$, $\beta: B \to C$, and $\gamma: C \to D$, then $\gamma \circ (\beta \circ \alpha) = (\gamma \circ \beta) \circ \alpha$.*

Proof. Note first that $\beta \circ \alpha$ and $\gamma \circ \beta$ make sense, and that $\gamma \circ (\beta \circ \alpha)$ and $(\gamma \circ \beta) \circ \alpha$ also make sense. Hence it is feasible to try to prove the lemma.

To prove that the two mappings are equal, we must prove that for each $a \in A$, $\big(\gamma \circ (\beta \circ \alpha)\big)(a) = \big((\gamma \circ \beta) \circ \alpha\big)(a)$. But by definition of composition of mappings, $\big(\gamma \circ (\beta \circ \alpha)\big)(a) = \gamma\big((\beta \circ \alpha)(a)\big)$, and $(\beta \circ \alpha)(a) = \beta(\alpha(a))$. Hence $\big(\gamma \circ (\beta \circ \alpha)\big)(a) = \gamma\big((\beta \circ \alpha)(a)\big) = \gamma\big(\beta(\alpha(a))\big)$. On the other hand, $\big((\gamma \circ \beta) \circ \alpha\big)(a) = (\gamma \circ \beta)(\alpha(a)) = \gamma\big(\beta(\alpha(a))\big)$. Thus the elements

$$\big(\gamma \circ (\beta \circ \alpha)\big)(a) \text{ and } \big((\gamma \circ \beta) \circ \alpha\big)(a)$$

are indeed equal for each $a \in A$. This proves the lemma.

Now let A, B be sets, and let α be a *one-to-one* mapping from A *onto* B. Then by the "onto-ness" of α, for each $b \in B$, there exists $a \in A$ such that $\alpha(a) = b$. By the "one-to-one-ness" of α, this a is unique. Hence the correspondence associating b to a is a mapping. We denote this mapping by α^{-1} and call it an *inverse* of α. Thus α^{-1} is a mapping from B to A, given by $\alpha^{-1}(b) = a$ if $\alpha(a) = b$. Note that, in order to define α^{-1}, we required that α is one-to-one and onto. The symbol α^{-1} is nonsense if α is not one-to-one and onto.

Note that if α is a one-to-one mapping from A onto B, then α^{-1} is a mapping from B to A. Hence both $\alpha \circ \alpha^{-1}$ and $\alpha^{-1} \circ \alpha$ make sense. Let $a \in A$, and let $\alpha(a) = b$; then $(\alpha^{-1} \circ \alpha)(a) = \alpha^{-1}(\alpha(a)) = \alpha^{-1}(b) = a$. Thus $\alpha^{-1} \circ \alpha$ is the identity mapping on A. Similarly, $\alpha \circ \alpha^{-1}$ is the identity mapping on B.

1.2.8 Definition. *Let A be any nonempty set. Let S(A) denote the set of all one-to-one mappings of A onto itself.*

The set $S(A)$ will be an important example in the discussion of the mathematical system known as a group. For that reason, we list the properties of $S(A)$ now for future reference.

1.2.9 Properties of S(A). *If α, β, γ are elements of S(A), then*

1) *$\alpha \circ \beta$ is an element of S(A),*

2) *$\alpha \circ (\beta \circ \gamma) = (\alpha \circ \beta) \circ \gamma$,*

3) *there exists an element ι (the identity mapping on A) in S(A) such that $\alpha \circ \iota = \iota \circ \alpha = \alpha$, and*

4) *there exists an element α^{-1} in S(A) such that $\alpha \circ \alpha^{-1} = \alpha^{-1} \circ \alpha = \iota$.*

We have verified properties (2), (3), and (4) in the foregoing discussion. Moreover, since α and β are mappings from A to A, $\alpha \circ \beta$ makes sense. That $\alpha \circ \beta$ is in fact one-to-one and onto is the result of 1.2.10, Exercise 5 below. That exercise definitely should be done before continuing.

1.2.10 Exercises

1. Give an example of a mapping which is one-to-one, but not onto.

2. Let I be the set of all integers. Which of the following mappings from I to I are one-to-one, and which are onto?

   a) $\alpha(i) = i - 4$ b) $\alpha(i) = i^2$
   c) $\alpha(i) = i^2 + 4$ d) $\alpha(i) = i^3$

3. Let R be the set of real numbers. Which of the following mappings from R to R are one-to-one, and which are onto?

   a) $\rho(x) = x + 6$ b) $\rho(x) = x^2 + 2$
   c) $\rho(x) = x^2 - 2$ d) $\rho(x) = x^3 - x + 2$

   (Recall that every cubic equation with real coefficients has a real root.)

4. Let P be the set of positive integers, and let E be the set of even positive integers. Give an example of mappings which satisfy the following conditions.

   a) $\alpha: P \to E$, one-to-one and onto
   b) $\alpha: P \to E$, one-to-one and not onto
   c) $\alpha: P \to E$, not one-to-one and onto
   d) $\alpha: P \to E$, not one-to-one and not onto
   e) $\alpha: E \to P$, one-to-one and onto
   f) $\alpha: E \to P$, one-to-one and not onto
   g) $\alpha: E \to P$, not one-to-one and onto
   h) $\alpha: E \to P$, not one-to-one and not onto

5. Prove the following. If $\alpha: A \to B$ and $\beta: B \to C$ are mappings, then

   a) $\beta \circ \alpha$ is one-to-one if both α and β are one-to-one, and
   b) $\beta \circ \alpha$ is onto if both α and β are onto.

6. A set A is said to be *infinite* if there is a one-to-one mapping from A onto a proper subset of A. Prove that the set I of all integers is infinite.

7. Two sets A, B are said to be of the same cardinality if there exists a one-to-one mapping from A onto B. If A and B are of the same cardinality, we write $|A| = |B|$. Prove the following.

   a) $|N| = |I|$ where $N = \{1, 2, 3, \ldots\}$ and I is the set of integers
   b) $|\{\text{real numbers } X \mid 0 < X \le 1\}| = |\{\text{real numbers } X \mid X \ge 1\}|$
   c) $|\{\text{real numbers } X \mid 1 \le X \le 4\}| = |\{\text{real numbers } X \mid 2 \le X \le 3\}|$
   d) $|I| = |E|$ where E is the set of even integers
   e) $|N| = |M|$ where $M = \{0, 10, 20, 30, \ldots\}$

8. By associating with each positive real number its natural logarithm, one has a candidate for a mapping. Is this correspondence a mapping? If so, is it one-to-one? Onto?

1.3 LOGIC AND METHODS OF PROOF

In this section we will discuss some elementary concepts of symbolic logic using an extremely intuitive and simple approach. While there are more elaborate and rigorous developments of these simple concepts, our approach here stems from the fact that we are interested in symbolic logic as it applies to the proofs of theorems we will encounter later. The material presented here is designed so that, once the concepts are understood, one need not revert to symbolic logic but can handle the English equivalents. Consequently, one must first learn to translate English sentences into symbolic form.

A *proposition* is a declarative sentence which is either true or false, *but not both*. For example, "Mary went to town" is a proposition; but "Study mathematics whenever you can" is not. Also "$2 + 6 = 10$" is a proposition which is in fact false, but since the truth or falsity of "$x + 6 = 10$" is unknown unless x is specified, "$x + 6 = 10$" is not a proposition. Lower case Latin letters, such as $p, q, r, \ldots$, are usually used as symbols for propositions.

Compound sentences are composed of one or more simple sentences joined by certain connectives. In the same way, we can join simple propositions by connectives and obtain a new proposition. If p and q are propositions, we shall be interested in the following propositions formed from p and q, using connectives which we will define later: "not p," "p and q," "p or q," "if p, then q," "p if and only if q."

The formal name for the connective *not* is *negation*, and its symbol is $\sim$. If p is a proposition, then $\sim p$ (read "not p") will be its negation. The proposition $\sim p$ is false whenever p is true, and p is false whenever $\sim p$ is true. This relationship is shown in the following truth table.

p	$\sim p$
T	F
F	T

Note that $\sim$ is meaningful when used with a simple proposition. This limitation does not apply to the other connectives.

The symbol for *and* is $\wedge$, and its formal name is *conjunction*. Thus, if p and q are propositions, $p \wedge q$ (read "p and q") is the conjunction of p and q. Naturally, the truth of $p \wedge q$ depends on the truth of p and q. We say $p \wedge q$ is a true proposition only when both p and q are true; if either p or q is false, then $p \wedge q$ is false. The following truth table serves as a definition of $\wedge$.

p	q	$p \wedge q$
T	T	T
T	F	F
F	T	F
F	F	F

In the English language, the connective *or* has more than one meaning. For instance, the exact meaning of the sentence "Mary or Ann went to town" is uncertain. It can mean two different things, depending upon the context in which the sentence is used. It could mean that one of the girls went to town and perhaps that both did; or it could mean that one went, but not both. In symbolic logic we must remove this obscurity. The connective *or* is denoted by $\vee$, and if p and q are propositions, we say that $p \vee q$ is the *disjunction* of p and q. The proposition $p \vee q$ is true whenever p is true or q is true (and thus $p \vee q$ is true whenever both p and q are true); and false when both p and q are false. Thus the truth table defining $\vee$ is as follows.

p	q	$p \vee q$
T	T	T
T	F	T
F	T	T
F	F	F

It is possible to define an *exclusive disjunction*, denoted by $\underline{\vee}$, such that if p and q are propositions, $p \underline{\vee} q$ is true when p is true or q is true and is false when both p and q are false and when both p and q are true. However, we will not use the exclusive disjunction in this text.

The next connective is the *conditional*, which is denoted by $\rightarrow$. If p and q are propositions, then $p \rightarrow q$ is read "if p, then q." Here is a specific example. Let p stand for the proposition "It is raining," and let q stand for "I will carry my umbrella." Then $p \rightarrow q$ is "If it is raining, then I will carry my umbrella." Now what of the truth of this new proposition $p \rightarrow q$? Certainly, if it is raining and I do carry my umbrella, this statement is true. Also, if it is raining and I do not carry my umbrella, the statement is false. But what if it is not raining? We avoid any dilemma by giving a precise definition of $\rightarrow$. If p and q are propositions, then $p \rightarrow q$ is false only when p is true and q is false; the truth table follows.

p	q	$p \rightarrow q$
T	T	T
T	F	F
F	T	T
F	F	T

Thus, to return to our example above, if it is not raining, then "If it is raining, then I will carry an umbrella" is true no matter whether I carry an umbrella or not.

The last connective we will consider is the *biconditional* ↔. If p and q are propositions, then p ↔ q is read "p if and only if q," and it is true when p and q are both true or both false, and it is false otherwise. The truth table follows.

p	q	$p \leftrightarrow q$
T	T	T
T	F	F
F	T	F
F	F	T

We can produce a multitude of propositions by combining simple propositions by means of one or more of these five connectives, ~, ∧, ∨, →, and ↔. For instance, if p, q, and r are propositions, we might consider the proposition $(p \wedge q) \rightarrow r$ and construct its truth table as follows.

p	q	r	$p \wedge q$	$(p \wedge q) \rightarrow r$
T	T	T	T	T
T	T	F	T	F
T	F	T	F	T
T	F	F	F	T
F	T	T	F	T
F	T	F	F	T
F	F	T	F	T
F	F	F	F	T

Two propositions are said to be *logically equivalent* (or simply *equivalent*) whenever their truth tables are identical; i.e., two propositions p and q are logically equivalent if p is true when q is true and p is false when q is false. We use the equals sign to denote that two propositions are logically equivalent. For example, $p \rightarrow q = \sim p \vee q$, as is shown in the following table.

p	q	$\sim p$	$\sim p \vee q$	$p \rightarrow q$
T	T	F	T	T
T	F	F	F	F
F	T	T	T	T
F	F	T	T	T

Consequently, we can substitute $\sim p \vee q$ for $p \to q$ in any situation and not produce any change. Another pair of logically equivalent propositions is $\sim(p \wedge q)$ and $\sim p \vee \sim q$. To see this, we compute their truth tables.

p	q	$p \wedge q$	$\sim(p \wedge q)$	$\sim p$	$\sim q$	$\sim p \vee \sim q$
T	T	T	F	F	F	F
T	F	F	T	F	T	T
F	T	F	T	T	F	T
F	F	F	T	T	T	T

Therefore $\sim(p \wedge q) = \sim p \vee \sim q$. This fact and 1.3.1, Exercise 4(b) below, are known as *De Morgan's Laws*, named after the English mathematician Augustus De Morgan (1806–1871). Note that $\sim(p \wedge q) = \sim p \vee \sim q$ says that the negation of "p and q" is "not-p or not-q." Thus the negation of the sentence "Bob and Ralph watched the game" is "Either Bob did not watch the game or Ralph did not watch the game." Practice in expressing the negation of sentences is provided in 1.3.1, Exercise 5.

Given two propositions p and q, there are four propositions which result from using $\to$ to join p and q. They are the following:

$$p \to q \quad \text{(conditional)},$$
$$q \to p \quad \text{(converse)},$$
$$\sim q \to \sim p \quad \text{(contrapositive)},$$
$$\sim p \to \sim q \quad \text{(inverse)}.$$

Of these four variations, the conditional and the contrapositive are logically equivalent, as are the converse and the inverse. To prove this assertion, one simply constructs the truth tables (see 1.3.1, Exercise 6 below).

Phrases which convey the idea of quantity are called *quantifiers*; for instance, "for all numbers x," "there exists a number x such that," and "for no numbers x" are all examples of quantifiers. The quantifier *all* is called the *universal quantifier*, and the quantifier *there exists* is called the *existential quantifier*. An alternative expression for "there exists" is "for some." The quantifier *no* (or *none*) is not given a name, since it is expressible in terms of the other two. For instance, "No horses are pink" is the same as "There does not exist a horse which is pink." Consequently, the *no* quantifier can be expressed in terms of the existential quantifier and the negation connective. Thus we need consider only two quantifiers—*all* and *some*.

It is important to consider the negation of statements involving quantifiers. The negation of the universal quantifier is the existential quantifier and a negation; e.g., the negation of "All boys are mean" is "There exists a boy who is not mean." Similarly, the negation of the existential quantifier is the universal quantifier and a negation; e.g., the negation of "Some girls are smart" is "No girls are smart." If quantifiers are used in connection with compound sentences, then quite often De Morgan's laws must be used in forming the negation.

Frequently an axiom of modern algebra is stated in the following form: "There exists a *unique* element x satisfying property P." This means that there exists an element x satisfying property P *and* there does not exist more than one x satisfying property P. To negate this "and" statement, we must use one of De Morgan's laws. "There does not exist an element x satisfying property P, or there exists more than one x satisfying property P."

Most theorems in modern algebra are stated as conditional statements; e.g., if x^2 is an odd number, then x is an odd number. (Here "odd number" means a positive integer not divisible by 2.) How would one prove that this statement is true? First observe that if p is "x^2 is an odd number" and if q is "x is an odd number," then the statement we want to prove is simply $p \rightarrow q$. But as exercise 9 below demonstrates, all the following propositions are logically equivalent to $p \rightarrow q$: $\sim q \rightarrow \sim p$, $p \wedge \sim q \rightarrow q$, $p \wedge \sim q \rightarrow \sim p$, and $p \wedge \sim q \rightarrow f$ where f is a proposition which is always false. Hence, to prove $p \rightarrow q$, it suffices to prove any of these logically equivalent propositions. When one proves $p \rightarrow q$ by proving one of these logically equivalent propositions, the proof is called an *indirect proof*. An indirect proof of "If x^2 is an odd number, then x is an odd number $(p \rightarrow q)$" would be as follows:

Suppose that x^2 is an odd number and that x is an even number $(p \wedge \sim q)$. Then $x = 2n$ for some positive integer n. Hence $x^2 = 2(2n^2)$, and so x^2 is even $(\sim p)$. Thus, if x^2 is an odd number, then x must also be odd.

In this argument we proved that the following proposition was true: $p \wedge \sim q \rightarrow \sim p$. Hence $p \rightarrow q$ is true.

1.3.1 Exercises

1. Let p denote "She is attractive," and let q denote "She is happy." Express the following sentences in symbolic form using p and q.

   a) If she is attractive, then she is happy.
   b) She is neither attractive nor happy.
   c) If she is unhappy, then she is unattractive.
   d) It is necessary for her to be attractive in order to be happy.
   e) She is unhappy or unattractive, but not both.
   f) For her to be happy means the same as for her to be attractive.

2. Construct truth tables for the statements of Exercise 1.

3. Construct truth tables for the following.

   a) $p \rightarrow (q \vee r)$ b) $(\sim p \vee r) \rightarrow \sim q$
   c) $(q \vee p) \leftrightarrow \sim p$ d) $(p \vee q) \rightarrow (\sim r \wedge s)$

4. By computing their truth tables, show that the following pairs of propositions are logically equivalent.

a) $p; \sim\sim p$
b) $\sim(p \lor q); \sim p \land \sim q$
c) $p \to q; p \land \sim q \to \sim p$
d) $p \leftrightarrow q; (p \to q) \land (q \to p)$

5. Form the negation of the following sentences.

a) It is raining or it is snowing.
b) If it rains today, I will stay home. (Recall that $p \to q = \sim p \lor q$.)
c) Mathematics is easy and either the wind is blowing or Carol is seventeen years old.
d) If Mary is going, then both Don and Dave are happy.
e) Either algebra is fun and tadpoles are frogs or shrugs are schrongies and Sue is not asleep.

6. a) If p and q are propositions, prove that the conditional $p \to q$ and the contrapositive $\sim q \to \sim p$ are logically equivalent. Prove that $p \land \sim q \to \sim p$ is also logically equivalent to $p \to q$.
   b) Restate the following sentence into two logically equivalent forms as suggested by (a): If it rains today, then I will carry an umbrella.

7. Identify the quantifiers in each of the following sentences.

a) All men are trustworthy.
b) Some men are short.
c) Some men are rich and happy.
d) For all x, there exists y such that $xy = 1$.
e) There exists e such that, for all z, $ez = z$.

8. Form the negation of each sentence in Exercise 7.

9. Prove that each of the following propositions is logically equivalent to the conditional $p \to q$.

a) $\sim q \to \sim p$
b) $p \land \sim q \to \sim p$
c) $p \land \sim q \to q$
d) $p \land \sim q \to f$ (where f is a proposition which is always false)

10. Supply indirect proofs for the following assertions.

a) If xy is an odd number, then x and y are both odd.
b) The quantity xy is even if and only if x is even or y is even.
c) If I am to pass this course, I must do homework regularly.

11. Let A, B, and C be sets contained in a set U. Prove the following pairs of sets are equal.

a) $A \cup (B \cap C); (A \cup B) \cap (A \cup C)$
b) $A \cap (B \cup C); (A \cap B) \cup (A \cap C)$
c) $\widetilde{A \cap B}; \tilde{A} \cup \tilde{B}$ (Here $\sim$ means "complement in U.")
d) $\widetilde{A \cup B}; \tilde{A} \cap \tilde{B}$

1.4 EQUIVALENCE RELATIONS

From our previous mathematical experience we realize the importance of the concept of equality. The notion of equivalence relation is a generalization of equality which will play an important role in our study of modern algebra.

A *relation* $\sim$ on a set A is a mapping which associates with each ordered pair (a, b) of elements of A a statement $a \sim b$ such that, first of all, $a \sim b$ makes sense, and second, $a \sim b$ is either true or false, *but never both*. Our interest in relations will be restricted to equivalence relations.

1.4.1 Definition. *A relation $\sim$ on a set A is an* **equivalence relation** *if $\sim$ has the following properties.*

1) $a \sim a$ *for all* $a \in A$ *(reflexive)*.

2) *If* $a \sim b$, *then* $b \sim a$ *for all* $a, b \in A$ *(symmetric)*.

3) *If* $a \sim b$ *and* $b \sim c$, *then* $a \sim c$ *for all* $a, b, c \in A$ *(transitive)*.

The symbol $a \sim b$ is read "a is equivalent to b"; if a is not equivalent to b, then we write $a \not\sim b$.

The relation $<$ on the integers is not an equivalence relation since it is not reflexive. The relation $\leq$ on the integers is reflexive and transitive, but not symmetric. Hence it also fails to be an equivalence relation. If we consider the set of all triangles in the plane, then "is congruent to" and "is similar to" are both equivalence relations on this set of triangles.

Now we consider an example of an important equivalence relation on the set I of all integers. Define

(1) $a \sim b$ if and only if $a - b$ is a multiple of 5.

Sometimes the notation $a \equiv b$ (mod 5) is used rather than $a \sim b$ for this equivalence relation. We will prove that (1) defines an equivalence relation on I. Let $a, b, c \in I$; then $a \sim a$ since $a - a = 0 = 0 \cdot 5$; i.e., $a - a$ is a multiple of 5. This proves that $\sim$ is reflexive. Now suppose $a \sim b$. This means that $a - b = 5n$ for some integer n, Hence $b - a = -(a - b) = -(5n) = 5(-n)$, and so $b - a$ is a multiple of 5. Thus $b \sim a$, which proves that $\sim$ is symmetric. Next we show that $\sim$ is transitive. Suppose $a \sim b$ and $b \sim c$. Then $a - b = 5m$ and $b - c = 5k$ for some integers m and k. Then $a - c = (a - b) + (b - c) = 5m + 5k = 5(m + k)$. Hence $a \sim c$. Therefore $\sim$ is an equivalence relation on I.

1.4.2 Definition. *Let $\sim$ be an equivalence relation on a set A. For each $a \in A$,*

$$[a] = \{x \in A \mid x \sim a\}$$

is called the **equivalence class of a,** *and a is called a* **representative** *of the equivalence class* $[a]$.

Thus [a] is the set of elements $x \in A$ which are equivalent to a. Notice that since $a \sim a$ by the reflexive property, $a \in [a]$ for all $a \in A$. Hence [a] is never the empty set.

Return now to the equivalence relation on I defined above; i.e., $a \sim b$ if $a - b$ is a multiple of 5. What are the equivalence classes associated with this equivalence relation? In particular, what integers belong to [2]? If $n \in [2]$, then by definition of equivalence class, $n \sim 2$. Hence $n - 2$ is a multiple of 5. Thus n is an integer of the form $n = 2 + 5k$ where k can be any integer. Thus

$$[2] = \{\ldots, -13, -8, -3, 2, 7, 12, 17, \ldots\}.$$

By a similar procedure, we see that

$$[0] = \{\ldots, -15, -10, -5, 0, 5, 10, 15, \ldots\},$$
$$[1] = \{\ldots, -14, -9, -4, 1, 6, 11, 16, \ldots\},$$
$$[3] = \{\ldots, -12, -7, -2, 3, 8, 13, 18, \ldots\}, \quad \text{and}$$
$$[4] = \{\ldots, -11, -6, -1, 4, 9, 14, 19, \ldots\}.$$

By examination of these equivalence classes, we see that every integer belongs to one of these five equivalence classes, and none of the equivalence classes have any elements in common. Therefore [0], [1], [2], [3], [4] form a *partition* of I. We will show that this is a property of equivalence classes in general.

1.4.3 Theorem. *Let* $\sim$ *be an equivalence relation on a set* A. *Then the following are true.*

1) *If* $a \in [b]$, *then* $[a] = [b]$.

2) $[a] = [b]$ *if and only if* $a \sim b$.

3) *If* $[a] \cap [b]$ *is not empty, then* $a \sim b$.

4) $[a] \cap [b]$ *is empty if and only if* $a \not\sim b$.

Proof. We will prove (1) and leave the rest for exercises. To prove (1), we must show that the two sets [a] and [b] are equal; i.e., that $[a] \subseteq [b]$ and $[b] \subseteq [a]$.

Assume that $a \in [b]$. Then by definition of equivalence classes, $a \sim b$. Now let $x \in [a]$. Then $x \sim a$. Since $x \sim a$ and $a \sim b$, by the transitive property of equivalence relations, $x \sim b$. Hence $x \in [b]$. Consequently we have shown that every element x belonging to [a] also belongs to [b]. Hence $[a] \subseteq [b]$.

Now let $y \in [b]$. Then $y \sim b$. Since $a \sim b$, by the symmetric property, $b \sim a$. Since $y \sim b$ and $b \sim a$, the transitive property implies that $y \sim a$. Hence $y \in [a]$. Therefore $[b] \subseteq [a]$. Finally, since $[a] \subseteq [b]$ and $[b] \subseteq [a]$, we have $[a] = [b]$, as asserted.

When proving parts (2) and (4) of Theorem 1.4.3, the reader must recall that if p, q are propositions, then $p \leftrightarrow q$ is equivalent to $(p \rightarrow q) \wedge (q \rightarrow p)$. Moreover, since (4) deals with a negative situation (that is, $[a] \cap [b]$ contains *no* elements and a is *not* equivalent to b), the parts of this proof are ideally suited to proofs by the indirect method discussed in the previous section.

As a result of Theorem 1.4.3, we get the following important theorem.

1.4.4 Theorem. *Let $\sim$ be an equivalence relation on a set A. Then the set of equivalence classes of $\sim$ form a partition of A.*

Proof. First, for every element $a \in A$, $a \sim a$ by the reflexive property, and so $a \in [a]$. Thus every element of A belongs to at least one equivalence class. Parts (2) and (3) of Theorem 1.4.3 show that no element can belong to two different equivalence classes. Therefore the set of equivalence classes forms a partition of A.

1.4.5 Exercises

1. Let T be the set of all triangles in the plane. Verify that "is similar to" is an equivalence relation on T.

2. Let I be the set of integers and define $\sim$ on I by $m \sim n$ if $m - n$ is a multiple of 4 for all $m, n \in I$. Prove that this is an equivalence relation on I. What are the equivalence classes associated with this equivalence relation? Prove that $[3] = [11]$.

3. Let I be the set of integers and define $\sim$ on I by $a \sim b$ if a is a multiple of b (i.e., $a \sim b$ if $a = bm$ for some $m \in I$) for all $a, b \in I$. Prove or disprove that $\sim$ is an equivalence relation.

4. Prove parts (2), (3), and (4) of Theorem 1.4.3.

5. Let $\sim$ be an equivalence relation on a set A. Given that $a, b, c, d \in A$ and $c \in [a]$, $d \in [b]$, and $[a] \neq [b]$, prove that $c \not\sim d$.

6. Let X be a given set of sets. Prove that "is of the same cardinality as" is an equivalence relation on X. (See 1.2.10, Exercise 7.)

7. Let I be the set of all integers, and define $\sim$ on I by $a \sim b$ if $a < b$ and $a > b$ for $a, b \in I$. Determine which of the properties of an equivalence relation $\sim$ satisfies.

8. The following argument shows that parts (2) and (3) of the definition of equivalence relation imply part (1); and hence that (1) can be dropped from the definition. By (2), $a \sim b$ implies $b \sim a$. Hence we have $a \sim b$ and $b \sim a$. Thus, by (3), $a \sim a$. Therefore (2) and (3) imply (1). This is not the case; (1) is necessary. Where is the fallacy in the above discussion?

1.5 BINARY OPERATIONS

The set I of integers is important to us since we have operations—namely, addition, subtraction, and multiplication—which can be used to combine integers to get other integers. Such operations are called binary operations on I. Some general sets have binary operations defined on them which allow the combining of two elements of the set to get another element of the set.

> ***1.5.1 Definition.*** *Let A be a nonempty set. A **binary operation** $\cdot$ **on A** is a correspondence which associates with each ordered pair (a, b) of elements of A a unique element $a \cdot b$ of A.*

An alternate definition of binary operation is: a mapping from the cross-product $A \times A$ to A where the image of (a, b) is $a \cdot b$. There are three words in Definition 1.5.1 which merit extra emphasis. The first is "each." If $\cdot$ is to be a binary operation on a set A, it must define $a \cdot b$ for every pair of elements a, b of A; i.e., there must not be any elements such that we cannot combine them. The next important word is "unique." For each pair of elements a, b of A, there must be only one "answer" $a \cdot b$ when we combine them. In particular, this says that if a_1, a_2, b_1, $b_2 \in A$ and if $a_1 = a_2$ and $b_1 = b_2$, then $a_1 \cdot b_1 = a_2 \cdot b_2$. When the operation in question has this "uniqueness," the operation is said to be *well defined*. The last word to be stressed is "of." For $\cdot$ to be a binary operation on A, $a \cdot b$ must be an element of A. Hence, for every $a, b \in A$, $a \cdot b \in A$. This property is usually called the *closure property*. Division is not a binary operation on the set of integers since it is not *closed;* e.g., 3 divided by 4 is not an integer.

A binary operation on a set may have additional properties. There are two in particular that are of interest in modern algebra.

> ***1.5.2 Definition.*** *Let $\cdot$ be a binary operation on a set A.*
>
> 1) The operation $\cdot$ is ***commutative*** *if $a \cdot b = b \cdot a$ for all $a, b \in A$.*
>
> 2) The operation $\cdot$ is ***associative*** *if $(a \cdot b) \cdot c = a \cdot (b \cdot c)$ for all $a, b, c \in A$.*

The binary operations addition $(+)$ and multiplication $(\cdot)$ on the integers are commutative and associative since $a + b = b + a$, $a \cdot b = b \cdot a$, $(a \cdot b) \cdot c = a \cdot (b \cdot c)$, and $(a + b) + c = a + (b + c)$ for all integers a, b, and c. In addition there is a relationship between $+$ and $\cdot$—namely, $a \cdot (b + c) = (a \cdot b) + (a \cdot c)$ and $(a + b) \cdot c = (a \cdot c) + (b \cdot c)$ for all $a, b, c \in I$. This extends to sets in general by the following definition.

> ***1.5.3 Definition.*** *Let $\cdot$ and $*$ be binary operations on a set A.*
>
> 1) The operation $*$ *is **left-distributive over** $\cdot$ if $a * (b \cdot c) = (a * b) \cdot (a * c)$ for all $a, b, c \in A$.*
>
> 2) The operation $*$ *is **right-distributive over** $\cdot$ if $(a \cdot b) * c = (a * c) \cdot (b * c)$ for all $a, b, c \in A$.*

1.5.4 Exercises

1. Prove or disprove that the following operations are binary operations on the indicated sets.
   a) The usual addition of integers on the set E of even integers.
   b) The usual addition of integers on the set O of odd integers.
   c) Let I be the set of integers. For all $a, b \in I$, define $a \,\textcircled{m}\, b$ to be any integer larger than both a and b.
   d) Let I be the set of integers. For all $a, b \in I$, define $a \,\$\, b$ to be the least common multiple of a and b.
   e) Let S be the set of all subsets of a given nonempty set A. For $B, C \in S$, define $B \cdot C = B \cap C$.

2. In each of the following, a set is given and a binary operation is defined on it. Prove or disprove that the binary operation is commutative and/or associative. Let I be the set of integers throughout this exercise.
   a) $I; a \cdot b = a - b$ for all $a, b \in I$.
   b) $I; a \,\#\, b = a + b + 1$ for all $a, b \in I$.
   c) $I; a \oplus b = a + b - ab$ for all $a, b \in I$.
   d) $T = \{a + b\sqrt{2} \mid a, b \in I\}$; usual multiplication of real numbers.
   e) E = set of even integers; $a \cdot b = 2ab$ for all $a, b \in E$.
   f) S = set of subsets of A; $B \cdot C = B \cap C$ for all $B, C \in S$.

3. Let I be the set of integers. Prove or disprove that the usual multiplication is left-distributive over each of the following.
   a) $a \cdot b = a - b$ for all $a, b \in I$.
   b) $a \,\#\, b = a + b + 1$ for all $a, b \in I$.
   c) $a \oplus b = a + b - ab$ for all $a, b \in I$.
   d) $a \,\$\, b$ = least common multiple of a and b for all $a, b \in I$.

1.6 DIVISION ALGORITHM FOR THE INTEGERS

In the material that follows we will sometimes require a lemma dealing with the set I of all integers. Basically, the lemma says that, given any two positive integers a and b, there exist integers q and r such that b goes into a a total of q times (possibly $q = 0$) with a remainder of r. We express this division process in the following equation $a = bq + r$; i.e., if we divide a by b, we get a quotient q and a remainder r. Also intuitively, we can always make the remainder r less than b or we can divide b into a more than q times. These ideas will be made precise in the lemma.

But first, observe that any nonempty set of nonnegative integers has a *least* element. This property of the set of nonnegative integers is known as the *well-ordering property*. Let S be a nonempty set of nonnegative integers. If $0 \in S$, then clearly 0 is the least element in S. If $0 \notin S$, then S will contain a least positive integer. We will require this property of the nonnegative integers for the proof of the lemma.

1.6.1 Lemma. *Let a, b be positive integers. Then there exist unique nonnegative integers q, r such that*

$$a = bq + r \quad \text{and} \quad 0 \leq r < b.$$

Proof. We must prove that there exist integers q and r with the properties described in the lemma, and then we must prove that q and r are unique. Let $S = \{a - bx \mid x \in I \text{ and } a - bx \geq 0\}$. Recall that a, b are given positive integers. Hence the elements $a - bx$ of S depend on x. Note that when $x = 0$, $a - bx = a$. Hence $a \in S$ since $a \geq 0$. Thus S is not empty. By the well-ordering property of the nonnegative integers discussed above, S must have a least element. Let this least element be $r = a - bq$. Then $r \geq 0$ and $a = bq + r$. Hence, if we show $r < b$, the lemma will be proved. Suppose this is false; i.e., suppose $r \geq b$. Then $r - b \geq 0$ and $r - b = (a - bq) - b = a - b(q + 1)$. Hence $r - b$ is of the form necessary to belong to S; i.e., $r - b \in S$. Moreover, since $b > 0$, we have $r - b < r$. We have shown that $r - b \in S$ and $r - b < r$; but r was chosen so that r was the *least* element of S. Consequently we have a contradiction and so $r < b$. This completes the proof of the existence part of the lemma.

To prove the uniqueness of q and r, we show that, for any nonnegative integers q_1 and r_1 such that $a = bq_1 + r_1$ and $0 \leq r_1 < b$, we must have $q = q_1$ and $r = r_1$. Suppose such a q_1 and r_1 exist. Without loss of generality, we may assume that $q \geq q_1$. Then, since b is positive, $b(q - q_1)$ is nonnegative. On the other hand, since $bq_1 + r_1 = bq + r$, $b(q - q_1) = r_1 - r$ so that $r_1 - r$ is nonnegative. Moreover, since $b > r_1$ and $b > r$, $b > r_1 - r$. Hence, if $q - q_1 \geq 1$, we must have $b(q - q_1) > r_1 - r$, which cannot be. Thus $q - q_1 = 0$. Hence $r_1 - r = 0$ and consequently $q = q_1$ and $r = r_1$. Therefore q and r are unique.

It should be pointed out that Lemma 1.6.1 is valid if a is any integer—positive, negative, or zero—and if b is any nonzero integer. This more general form of the division algorithm will be proved in a later chapter.

There are several terms which will be used frequently and with which most students are familiar. To avoid any ambiguity, we give precise definitions of these terms here. In a later chapter we will explore thoroughly the implications of the definition.

1.6.2 Definition. *Let a and b be integers, $a \neq 0$. Then a is said to **divide** b if there exists an integer c such that $b = ac$. Alternate expressions for "a divides b" are "a is a divisor of b," "a is a factor of b," and "b is a multiple of a."*

1.7 MATHEMATICAL INDUCTION

In this section we establish the Principle of Mathematical Induction, which is the basis of proofs throughout the remainder of the book. First, the following is essential.

__1.7.1 Lemma.__ Let Q be a set of positive integers with the following properties.

1) $1 \in Q$.

2) *If k is a positive integer such that $k \in Q$, then $k + 1 \in Q$.*

Then Q is the set of all positive integers.

Proof. Assume that Q is not the set of all positive integers, and let R be the set of all positive integers not in Q. Then R has a smallest element, r. Then by (1), $r \neq 1$; hence $r - 1$ is a positive integer and $r - 1 \notin R$. Thus $r - 1 \in Q$. Applying (2) when $k = r - 1$ implies that $k + 1 = r \in Q$. But r was chosen as an element of R so that $r \notin Q$. This contradiction establishes the lemma.

__1.7.2 Principle of Mathematical Induction.__ Suppose that with each positive integer n there is associated a statement S_n. If

1) S_1 *is true and*

2) *if k is a positive integer such that S_k is true, then S_{k+1} is true;*

then S_n is true for all positive integers n.

Proof. Let Q be the set of positive integers n such that S_n is true. Then Q satisfies the hypothesis of Lemma 1.7.1. Therefore Q is the set of all positive integers; that is, S_n is true for all positive integers n.

As an illustration of the use of the Principle of Mathematical Induction, let us consider a simple example from college algebra:

$$1 + 2 + \cdots + n = n(n + 1)/2$$

for all positive integers n. To prove this, let S_n be the statement "$1 + 2 + \cdots + n = n(n + 1)/2$". Then S_n says that the sum of the first n positive integers is $n(n + 1)/2$. The statement S_1 simply says that $1 = (1 \cdot 2)/2$; so S_1 is true. Suppose that k is any positive integer such that S_k is true; that is, suppose that $1 + 2 + \cdots + k = k(k + 1)/2$. By adding $k + 1$ to both sides, we get

$$1 + 2 + \cdots + k + k + 1 = k(k + 1)/2 + k + 1$$
$$= (k + 1)(k + 2)/2.$$

Hence S_{k+1} is true. Thus, by the Principle of Mathematical Induction, S_n is true for all positive integers n; hence the result holds.

Another application of the Principle of Mathematical Induction is in making *recursive* (or *inductive*) *definitions.* When one gives a definition which depends upon a positive integer n, the definition is often done recursively. For example, let a be any integer. We wish to define formally what is meant by a^n where n can be any positive integer. First, define $a^1 = a$. Then, if k is any positive integer such that a^k is defined, define $a^{k+1} = a^k \cdot a$. If S_n

is the statement "a^n is defined," then the Principle of Mathematical Induction shows that a^n is defined for all positive integers n.

1.7.3 Exercises

1. Prove the following formulas from college algebra.
   a) $1 + 2^2 + 3^2 + \cdots + n^2 = n(n + 1)(2n + 1)/6$.
   b) $2 + 4 + 6 + \cdots + 2n = n(n + 1)$.
   c) $3 + 3^2 + 3^3 + \cdots + 3^n = 3(3^n - 1)/2$.
   d) $a + (a + d) + (a + 2d) + \cdots + (a + nd) = (n + 1)(2a + nd)/2$.
   e) $a + ar + ar^2 + \cdots + ar^n = a(1 - r^{n+1})/(1 - r)$.

2. Let x, y be integers and let m, n be positive integers. Prove the following rules for exponents. Use the definition given above.
   a) $(xy)^n = x^n y^n$.
   b) $x^m x^n = x^{m+n}$. (Hint: Let S_n be "$x^m x^n = x^{m+n}$ for all positive integers m.")
   c) $(x^m)^n = x^{mn}$.

3. Use the fact that the set of positive integers is well ordered (every nonempty set of positive integers has a smallest element) to prove the following:

   Strong Principle of Mathematical Induction. Suppose that with each positive integer n there is associated a statement S_n. Suppose that

   1) S_1 is true and,

   2) if k is a positive integer such that S_i is true for all $i < k$, then S_k is true.
   Then S_n is true for all positive integers n.

4. Show that the Strong Principle of Mathematical Induction is equivalent to the Principle of Mathematical Induction (and hence is really not *stronger* at all).

ADDITIONAL REFERENCES FOR CHAPTER 1

COPI, IRVING M., *Symbolic Logic*, second edition, New York: Macmillan (1965).

KEMENY, JOHN G., HAZELTON MIRKIL, JO LAURIE SNELL, and GERALD L. THOMPSON, *Finite Mathematical Structures*, Englewood Cliffs, New Jersey: Prentice-Hall (1958).

MAY, KENNETH O., *Elements of Modern Mathematics*, Reading, Massachusetts: Addison-Wesley (1959).

McCOY, NEAL H., *Introduction to Modern Algebra*, Boston: Allyn and Bacon (1960).

OHMER, MERLIN M., CLAYTON V. ANCOIN, and MARION J. CORTEZ, *Elementary Contemporary Mathematics*, New York: Blaisdell (1964).

CHAPTER 2

GROUPS

In this chapter, we begin the study of our first algebraic system—a group. We will define group and then develop some rudimentary properties. Then we will consider several examples of groups and observe that the properties hold in them. Then we will study subgroups, cosets and Lagrange's Theorem, normal subgroups and factor groups, and homomorphisms—in that order.

A group is merely a nonempty set on which there is defined a binary operation satisfying certain properties. These properties are stated as axioms which the binary operation must satisfy. There is a certain naturalness about the axioms; they are not chosen at random. The study of an abstract algebraic system results from the observation that several concrete examples have a binary operation which does satisfy the axioms. Consequently, by studying an algebraic system abstractly, one is, in a sense, studying all concrete examples whose binary operation satisfies the axioms.

2.1 DEFINITION OF A GROUP

2.1.1 Definition. *A nonempty set of elements G is said to form a **group** if on G there is defined a binary operation denoted by · satisfying the following axioms.*

G1 *For all $a, b \in G$, $a \cdot b \in G$*   *(closure law).*

G2 *For all $a, b, c \in G$, $(a \cdot b) \cdot c = a \cdot (b \cdot c)$*   *(associative law).*

G3 *There exists an element $e \in G$ such that $a \cdot e = e \cdot a = a$ for all $a \in G$*   *(the existence of an identity element in G).*

G4 *For every $a \in G$, there exists an element $b \in G$ such that $a \cdot b = b \cdot a = e$*   *(existence of inverses in G).*

Now let us examine these axioms closely. Axiom G1 is actually redundant. The fact that · is a binary operation on G guarantees that G is closed under ·. But G1 is included traditionally in the definition of a group to emphasize the closure property of the binary operation. The axiom G2 simply states that the binary operation is associative. In axioms G3 and G4, one must pay particular attention to the quantifiers. Axiom G3 guarantees the existence of an element e, called an identity element, such that $a \cdot e = e \cdot a = a$ for all a in G; that is, e combined with any element a of G is just the element a again. Notice that there is one e which must "work" for all a in G. Also, the axiom does not state that e is unique; that is, there may be (as far as we know) more than one element in G which satisfies axiom G3. Axiom G4 states that, corresponding to each element a in G, there is an element b in G such that $a \cdot b = b \cdot a = e$. The element b may "work" with only this one a. However, each element a of G has such a b. Moreover, axiom G4 does not guarantee the uniqueness of b; thus, for any fixed a in G, there may be several elements b such that $a \cdot b = b \cdot a = e$. The essential difference between the quantification in axioms G3 and G4 is this: G3 is a "there exists, for all" statement, whereas G4 is a "for all, there exists" statement. It is imperative that the reader distinguish between these two ideas. We will prove in the next section that, in fact, the identity element and inverses specified in axioms G3 and G4 are unique.

A group may have many properties other than those specified by the axioms. One property enjoyed by many important groups is that the binary operation is commutative. These groups are so important that we make the following definition.

2.1.2 Definition. *A group G is said to be* **abelian** (*or* **commutative**) *if the following axiom is satisfied.*

$$\text{For all } a, b \in G, a \cdot b = b \cdot a.$$

The term "abelian group" is most commonly used for groups which also satisfy the axiom above. The name is derived from Niels Henrik Abel (1802–1829), a famous Norwegian mathematician, but its use is so common that "abelian" is usually not capitalized. The reader must be wary of unconsciously assuming that all groups are abelian.

2.1.3 Examples

1. Consider the set I of all integers with the usual addition as binary operation. That the closure and associative laws hold is a well-known property of I. Zero is the identity element of I, and for each $n \in I$, $-n$ is its inverse. Hence addition as a binary operation on I satisfies the axioms G1–G4. Hence I is a group. It is also well known that for all $m, n \in I$, $m + n = n + m$. Hence I is an abelian group.

2. Now consider the set I of all integers with the usual multiplication as binary operation. The element 1 is the identity element since, for all $n \in I$, $n \cdot 1 = 1 \cdot n = n$. But there is no element $m \in I$ such that $3 \cdot m = m \cdot 3 = 1$. Hence I with the usual multiplication is *not* a group.

3. This example is quite different from those above. Let G be the set $\{u, v, w, x\}$, and define an operation $\cdot$ on G by the following table.

$\cdot$	u	v	w	x
u	u	v	w	x
v	v	u	x	w
w	w	x	v	u
x	x	w	u	v

The table is used in the following way: To find $v \cdot w$, find v in the vertical column at the left and w in the horizontal column at the top. Then $v \cdot w$ is determined by finding where the row of v crosses the column of w; hence $v \cdot w = x$.

By observation, it is clear that whenever any two elements of G are combined, the result is an element of G. Hence G1 holds. Before considering the associative law, notice that u is the identity of G. To verify associativity, one must consider all possible ways of combining three elements of G. However, since u is the identity of G, the investigation may be restricted to all possible ways of combining v, w, and x. But there are still 27 possibilities for which the associativity must be checked. Consequently, the details are not included. All that remains to show that G is a group is to find an inverse for each element of G. However, from the table it is apparent that u and v are their own inverses and w and x are inverses of each other. Hence G is a group. It is left for the reader to show that G is an abelian group.

4. Recall that the set of all rational numbers is the set of all fractions of the form a/b where a, $b \in I$ and $b \neq 0$. Then the set L of all *nonzero* rational numbers forms a group with respect to multiplication. We know that G1 and G2 hold. Since $1 = 1/1$, we have $1 \in L$ and for any $a/b \in L$, $1(a/b) = (a/b)1 = a/b$. Hence G3 holds. Moreover, since for any $a/b \in L$, a/b must be nonzero, then a itself must be a nonzero integer. Thus $b/a \in L$ and $(b/a)(a/b) = (a/b)(b/a) = 1/1 = 1$. Hence G3 holds.

5. Our own experience provides us with the necessary information to prove that the set Q of *all* rational numbers is a group with the usual addition; also that the set R of all real numbers is a group with the usual addition. The proofs that Q and R are groups are left as exercises.

2.2 SIMPLE PROPERTIES OF GROUPS

In axiom G3 of the definition of a group, we asserted the existence of an identity element and remarked that the axiom did not guarantee its uniqueness. In the following theorem, we prove that an identity element of a group is unique. But first, let us examine what this means. That an identity element of a group is unique means that there is exactly one identity element. Since we know by axiom G3 that there is at least one identity element, the negation of "an identity element is unique" is "there exists more than one identity element." Thus, to prove that an identity element is unique, we will assume that there are more than one and then show that they must all be equal. This method of proving uniqueness is, in general, "standard operating procedure."

2.2.1 Theorem. *Let G be a group with binary operation ·. The identity element of G is unique.*

Proof. Assume that G has two identity elements, e and f. Then, since e is an identity element of G,

(1) $\qquad\qquad a \cdot e = e \cdot a = a \qquad$ for all $a \in G$.

Similarly, since f is an identity element of G,

(2) $\qquad\qquad a \cdot f = f \cdot a = a \qquad$ for all $a \in G$.

In particular, since (1) is true for all $a \in G$, it must also be true for $a = f$; that is,

(3) $\qquad\qquad\qquad f \cdot e = e \cdot f = f.$

Also (2) must be true for $a = e$; consequently

(4) $\qquad\qquad\qquad e \cdot f = f \cdot e = e.$

By comparing (3) and (4), we see that $e = f$. Hence an identity element of G is unique.

Before proceeding, we will prove the following theorem.

2.2.2 Theorem (Cancellation Laws). *Let a, b, c be arbitrary elements of a group G with binary operation ·. Then the following are true.*

i) *If $a \cdot b = a \cdot c$, then $b = c$.*

ii) *If $a \cdot c = b \cdot c$, then $a = b$.*

Proof. We will prove (i) and leave the proof of (ii) as an exercise. Suppose $a \cdot b = a \cdot c$. By axiom G4 of a group, a has an inverse in G; that is, there exists an element s in G such that $a \cdot s = s \cdot a = e$ where e is the identity element of G. Since · is a binary operation,

(5) $\qquad\qquad\qquad s \cdot (a \cdot b) = s \cdot (a \cdot c).$

But

$$\begin{aligned} s \cdot (a \cdot b) &= (s \cdot a) \cdot b &&\text{(associative law)}\\ &= e \cdot b &&\text{(definition of inverse)}\\ &= b. &&\text{(definition of identity)} \end{aligned}$$

Similarly,

$$s \cdot (a \cdot c) = (s \cdot a) \cdot c = e \cdot c = c.$$

From (5) and these computations, we see that $b = c$, as asserted, Thus proving (i).

The fourth axiom in the definition of a group guarantees the existence of an inverse for each element. Let a be an arbitrary element of a group G. Then there exists an element $b \in G$ such that $a \cdot b = b \cdot a = e$ where e is the identity element of G. The next theorem proves that this b is unique. The method of proving uniqueness is the same as that used above.

2.2.3 Theorem. *Let a be an arbitrary element of a group G with binary operation . Then an inverse of a is unique.*

Proof. Assume that b and c are both inverses of a. Then by definition of an inverse of a,

(6) $$a \cdot b = b \cdot a = e$$

and

(7) $$a \cdot c = c \cdot a = e.$$

From (6) and (7) we see that $a \cdot b = a \cdot c$. Hence, by the cancellation law, $b = c$. Thus an inverse of a is unique.

As a result of Theorems 2.2.1 and 2.2.3, we can speak of *the* identity element of a group and, for each element a of a group, *the* inverse of a. We will usually use e to denote the identity element of a group, and for the inverse of an element a we usually use the symbol a^{-1}. Hence, for an element a of a group,

$$a \cdot a^{-1} = a^{-1} \cdot a = e.$$

The next two theorems establish some properties of inverses.

2.2.4 Theorem. *If G is a group, then $(a^{-1})^{-1} = a$ for all $a \in G$.*

Proof. Observe that $(a^{-1})^{-1}$ is the inverse of a^{-1}. Hence

$$(a^{-1})^{-1} \cdot (a^{-1}) = (a^{-1}) \cdot (a^{-1})^{-1} = e.$$

But since $a \cdot a^{-1} = a^{-1} \cdot a = e$, then a is also the inverse of a^{-1}. Consequently $(a^{-1})^{-1}$ and a are both inverses of a^{-1}. Since the inverse of a^{-1} is unique, we must have $(a^{-1})^{-1} = a$.

2.2.5 Theorem. *If G is a group, then $(a \cdot b)^{-1} = b^{-1} \cdot a^{-1}$ for all $a, b \in G$.*

Proof. By definition $(a \cdot b)^{-1}$ is the inverse of $a \cdot b$. But

$$
\begin{aligned}
(a \cdot b) \cdot (b^{-1} \cdot a^{-1}) &= ((a \cdot b) \cdot b^{-1}) \cdot a^{-1} && \text{(associative law)} \\
&= (a \cdot (b \cdot b^{-1})) \cdot a^{-1} && \text{(associative law)} \\
&= (a \cdot e) \cdot a^{-1} && \text{(definition of } b^{-1}) \\
&= a \cdot a^{-1} && \text{(definition of } e) \\
&= e. && \text{(definition of } a^{-1})
\end{aligned}
$$

Similarly,

$$(b^{-1} \cdot a^{-1}) \cdot (a \cdot b) = ((b^{-1} \cdot a^{-1}) \cdot a) \cdot b = (b^{-1} \cdot (a^{-1} \cdot a)) \cdot b$$
$$= (b^{-1} \cdot e) \cdot b = b^{-1} \cdot b = e.$$

These computations show that $b^{-1} \cdot a^{-1}$ is the inverse of $a \cdot b$. Hence, since the inverse of $a \cdot b$ is unique, we must have

$$(a \cdot b)^{-1} = b^{-1} \cdot a^{-1}.$$

Since the group G in Theorem 2.2.5 may not be abelian $b^{-1} \cdot a^{-1}$ may not equal $a^{-1} \cdot b^{-1}$. The reader must be careful not to assume that these are equal.

One method of classifying groups is by consideration of the number of elements in the group. Hence we make the following definition.

2.2.6 Definition. *Let G be a group. If G has a finite number of elements, say n, then we say that the **order of G** is n. We write this symbolically by $o(G) = n$, and in this case we say G is a **finite group**. If G does not have a finite number of elements, we say G is an **infinite group**.*

If a is an element of a group G, then a times itself is $a \cdot a$. If we multiply this by a again, we get $(a \cdot a) \cdot a$. From our past experience with the integers and the real numbers, we expect that there is a shorthand method of denoting the repeated multiplication of a by itself. Hence we make the following definition.

2.2.7 Definition. *Let a be an element of a group G with identity element e. Define*

$$a^0 = e$$
$$a^1 = a,$$
$$a^2 = a \cdot a,$$

and whenever a^k is defined for a positive integer k, define

$$a^{k+1} = a^k \cdot a.$$

Then, by the Principle of Mathematical Induction, (1.7.2), a^n is defined for all nonnegative integers n. Furthermore, define

$$a^{-n} = (a^{-1})^n$$

for all positive integers n. Then a^n is defined for all integers n.

Next we see that this definition of exponents provides the usual rules of exponents.

2.2.8 Theorem. *Let G be a group and let a, b be arbitrary elements of G. Then*

1) $a^m \cdot a^n = a^{m+n}$ for all positive integers m and n,

2) $(a^m)^n = a^{mn}$ *for all positive integers m and n, and*

3) *if G is abelian, $(a \cdot b)^n = a^n \cdot b^n$ for all positive integers n.*

Proof. We will prove (1) and leave (2) and (3) as exercises. The proofs of all three statements use mathematical induction. Let $P(n)$ be the statement "$a^m \cdot a^n = a^{m+n}$ for all positive integers m." Then $P(1)$ is simply "$a^m \cdot a^1 = a^{m+1}$ for all positive integers m." This is true by the definition of a^{m+1}. Assume that $P(k)$ holds for some positive integer k. Then

$$
\begin{aligned}
a^m \cdot a^{k+1} &= a^m \cdot (a^k \cdot a) && \text{(definition of } a^{k+1}) \\
&= (a^m \cdot a^k) \cdot a && \text{(associative law)} \\
&= a^{m+k} \cdot a && \text{[by } P(k)] \\
&= a^{m+k+1} && \text{(definition of } a^{m+k+1})
\end{aligned}
$$

for all positive integers m. Hence $P(k+1)$ is true. Thus, by the Principle of Mathematical Induction, $P(n)$ is true for all positive integers n, thus proving (1).

2.2.9 Remark. It is important to observe that the results of Theorem 2.2.8 hold for *all* integers m and n—positive, negative, or zero. Clearly, since $a^0 = e$, the results hold if either m or n is zero. Let us investigate the validity of part (1) in cases in which m or n is a negative integer. Parts (2) and (3) can be handled similarly. Suppose m and n are both negative. Then $-m$ and $-n$ are both positive. Hence,

$$
\begin{aligned}
a^m \cdot a^n &= (a^{-1})^{-m} \cdot (a^{-1})^{-n} && \text{(definition)} \\
&= (a^{-1})^{-m-n} && \text{[(1) above]} \\
&= (a^{-1})^{-(m+n)} && \text{(notation)} \\
&= a^{m+n} && \text{(definition).}
\end{aligned}
$$

Now consider what happens when one exponent is positive and the other is negative. We consider one possibility; the other is similar. Suppose $m > 0$, $n < 0$, and $-n < m$. Let $p = -n$; then p is positive. Hence,

$$
\begin{aligned}
a^m \cdot a^n &= (a^{m-p} \cdot a^p) \cdot a^{-p} && \text{[(1) above]} \\
&= a^{m-p} \cdot (a^p \cdot a^{-p}) && \text{(associativity).}
\end{aligned}
$$

But by a simple induction argument, it can be shown that $a^p \cdot a^{-p} = e$ for all positive integers p. Hence we have $a^m \cdot a^n = a^{m-p} = a^{m+n}$ since $p = -n$.

2.3 EXAMPLES OF GROUPS

In this section we present many examples of groups. A thorough study of each of these examples should develop an intuitive appreciation of groups. In particular, one should note that while all the groups must have the properties required by the axioms G1–G4, whatever additional properties the groups possess may vary widely. The reader should verify that all axioms G1–G4 hold for each example.

Example 1. Let G be the set $\{u, v, w, x\}$ and define $\cdot$ by the table

$\cdot$	u	v	w	x
u	x	w	u	v
v	w	x	v	u
w	u	v	w	x
x	v	u	x	w

Is G a group? You may assume that G is associative. What is the identity? What is the inverse of each element? Is it abelian?

Example 2. Let I be the set of all integers, and let n be a fixed positive integer. We have shown in Section 1.4 that "for $a, b \in I$, $a \equiv b \pmod{n}$ if $a - b$ is a multiple of n" is an equivalence relation on I. For $m \in I$, let $[m]$ denote the equivalence class of m. Let

$$I/(n) = \{[0], [1], [2], \ldots, [n-1]\};$$

i.e., the elements of the set $I/(n)$ are equivalence classes.

Next we show that every element of I belongs to exactly one of the equivalence classes in $I/(n)$. Let k be an integer. By the division algorithm for the integers (Lemma 1.6.1), there exist integers q, r such that $k = qn + r$ and $0 \leq r < n$. Then $k - r = qn$ and so $k \equiv r \pmod{n}$. Thus $k \in [r]$. Since $0 \leq r < n$, then $[r]$ must be one of the elements of $I/(n)$. Hence k belongs to one of the elements of $I/(n)$. Since the elements of $I/(n)$ are distinct equivalence classes, they have no elements in common. This proves our assertion.

Now we define an addition on $I/(n)$. For $[m], [k] \in I/(n)$, set

$$[m] + [k] = [m + k];$$

i.e., the sum of the equivalence class of m and the equivalence class of k is the equivalence class of $k + m$. Hence the sum of the equivalence classes $[m]$ and $[k]$ seems to depend on the integers m and k. But if m_1 and k_1 are integers such that $m_1 \in [m]$ and $k_1 \in [k]$, then $[m_1] = [m]$ and $[k_1] = [k]$. Hence

$$[m] + [k] = [m_1] + [k_1] = [m_1 + k_1].$$

In order to prove that this addition is a binary operation, we must prove that

$$[m_1 + k_1] = [m + k];$$

i.e., for $[m]$ and $[k] \in I/(n)$ there exists a *unique* $[m] + [k] \in I/(n)$. When this has been proved, one says that the addition is *well defined*. Suppose $[m] = [m_1]$ and $[k] = [k_1]$. Then $m \equiv m_1 \pmod{n}$ and $k \equiv k_1 \pmod{n}$.

Hence $m = m_1 + qn$ and $k = k_1 + pn$ for some integers p, q. Then

$$m + k = m_1 + k_1 + (q + p)n,$$

and so

$$m + k \equiv m_1 + k_1 \pmod{n}.$$

Therefore $[m + k] = [m_1 + k_1]$, and so the addition is well defined.

Finally we prove that $I/(n)$ is a group with the binary operation we have defined. We have already seen that axiom G1 holds. Let $[m], [k], [q] \in I/(n)$. Then

$$\begin{aligned}
([m] + [k]) + [q] &= [m + k] + [q] \\
&= [(m + k) + q] \\
&= [m + (k + q)] \qquad \text{(associative law for } I) \\
&= [m] + [k + q] \\
&= [m] + ([k] + [q]).
\end{aligned}$$

Hence G2 holds. Moreover, $[0] \in I/(n)$ and is the identity of $I/(n)$; and for $[m] \in I/(n)$, $[n - m] \in I/(n)$ and $[m] + [n - m] = [n] = [0]$ and $[n - m] + [m] = [n] = [0]$. Hence $[n - m]$ is the inverse of $[m]$. Thus $I/(n)$ is a group.

As an illustration, the addition table for $I/(5)$ is given below. For simplification, the brackets [ ] around the elements of $I/(5)$ are omitted; hence 3 means [3], etc.

+	0	1	2	3	4
0	0	1	2	3	4
1	1	2	3	4	0
2	2	3	4	0	1
3	3	4	0	1	2

Example 3. Let M be the set of all symbols of the form

$$\begin{pmatrix} a & b \\ c & d \end{pmatrix}$$

where $a, b, c, d \in I$. The set M is called the set of 2×2 *matrices over* I. An individual element of M is a *matrix*. Two matrices are *equal* if they are identical; i.e.,

$$\begin{pmatrix} a & b \\ c & d \end{pmatrix} = \begin{pmatrix} e & f \\ g & h \end{pmatrix}$$

if and only if $a = e, b = f, c = g$, and $d = h$. Define an addition on M by setting

$$\begin{pmatrix} a & b \\ c & d \end{pmatrix} + \begin{pmatrix} e & f \\ g & h \end{pmatrix} = \begin{pmatrix} a + e & b + f \\ c + g & d + h \end{pmatrix}$$

for all

$$\begin{pmatrix} a & b \\ c & d \end{pmatrix}, \begin{pmatrix} e & f \\ g & h \end{pmatrix} \in M.$$

Then M is an abelian group with this operation. The identity is

$$\begin{pmatrix} 0 & 0 \\ 0 & 0 \end{pmatrix}$$

and the inverse of

$$\begin{pmatrix} a & b \\ c & d \end{pmatrix} \quad \text{is} \quad \begin{pmatrix} -a & -b \\ -c & -d \end{pmatrix}.$$

Notice that

$$\begin{pmatrix} -a & -b \\ -c & -d \end{pmatrix} \in M$$

since, for all a, b, c, $d \in I$, $-a$, $-b$, $-c$, $-d \in I$. The remaining details are left as an exercise.

Example 4. In Section 1.2 we discussed the set $S(A)$ of all one-to-one mappings from a nonempty set A onto itself. The statement of 1.2.9 lists the properties of $S(A)$, which were proved as theorems or exercises in that section. However, the properties listed in 1.2.9 are precisely the properties needed to prove that $S(A)$ is a group with composition of mappings as binary operation. If A contains more than two elements, then $S(A)$ is not abelian. Prove it!

Example 5. Let $x_1, x_2, \ldots, x_n$ be any n symbols. A *permutation* of $x_1, x_2, \ldots, x_n$ is a one-to-one mapping from the set $\{x_1, x_2, \ldots, x_n\}$ onto itself. As was noted in Example 4, the set of all permutations of $x_1, x_2, \ldots, x_n$ is a group where the operation is composition of mappings. This group is denoted by S_n and is called the *symmetric group of n symbols*. Even though S_n is a special case of $S(A)$, it is sufficiently important in the study of groups to merit special consideration.

To illustrate the principles involved without the confusion of details, we will consider the case when $n = 4$. Then the mapping α defined by

$$\alpha(x_1) = x_2, \qquad \alpha(x_2) = x_3, \qquad \alpha(x_3) = x_1, \qquad \alpha(x_4) = x_4$$

is a permutation on x_1, x_2, x_3, x_4. It seems advisable to develop a shorthand notation for the mapping α rather than writing the α and x's so many times. Notice that the essential thing about α is that the first symbol is mapped to the second, the second to the third, the third to the first, and the fourth to the fourth. The notation

$$\alpha = \begin{pmatrix} 1 & 2 & 3 & 4 \\ 2 & 3 & 1 & 4 \end{pmatrix}$$

will be used to represent the permutation α. The 1, 2, 3, and 4 of the top row represent the first, second, third, and fourth symbols respectively, and the bottom row contains their images; i.e., the image of each symbol is directly below it. Hence the permutation

$$\beta(x_1) = x_3, \qquad \beta(x_2) = x_4, \qquad \beta(x_3) = x_1, \qquad \beta(x_4) = x_2$$

could be represented by

$$\beta = \begin{pmatrix} 1 & 2 & 3 & 4 \\ 3 & 4 & 1 & 2 \end{pmatrix}.$$

For ease in discussing these permutations, one usually replaces x_1 by 1, x_2 by 2, etc. Hence α and β are thought of as permutations on the set $\{1, 2, 3, 4\}$.

Since α and β are simply mappings, we can compose them as usual to give $\beta \circ \alpha$; hence

$$\beta \circ \alpha = \begin{pmatrix} 1 & 2 & 3 & 4 \\ 3 & 4 & 1 & 2 \end{pmatrix} \circ \begin{pmatrix} 1 & 2 & 3 & 4 \\ 2 & 3 & 1 & 4 \end{pmatrix}$$

$$= \begin{pmatrix} 1 & 2 & 3 & 4 \\ 4 & 1 & 3 & 2 \end{pmatrix}.$$

To obtain this result, first recall that the mapping on the right must be applied first. What is the image of 1 under this composition? The mapping α takes 1 to 2 and β takes 2 to 4; hence $\beta \circ \alpha$ takes 1 to 4. Similarly, 2 goes to 3, and then 3 goes to 1; hence 2 goes to 1. The element 3 goes to 1, which in turn goes to 3, whereas 4 goes to 4, and then 4 goes to 2. Hence $\beta \circ \alpha$ maps 1, 2, 3, 4 onto 4, 1, 3, 2 respectively. Now what of $\alpha \circ \beta$?

$$\alpha \circ \beta = \begin{pmatrix} 1 & 2 & 3 & 4 \\ 2 & 3 & 1 & 4 \end{pmatrix} \circ \begin{pmatrix} 1 & 2 & 3 & 4 \\ 3 & 4 & 1 & 2 \end{pmatrix}$$

$$= \begin{pmatrix} 1 & 2 & 3 & 4 \\ 1 & 4 & 2 & 3 \end{pmatrix}.$$

This result is obtained as above. It must be kept in mind that the mapping on the right is applied first. Observe that $\beta \circ \alpha \neq \alpha \circ \beta$, since the image of 1 under $\alpha \circ \beta$ is 1, and the image of 1 under $\beta \circ \alpha$ is 4.

Returning to S_n, we can easily see that in general a permutation on the n symbols $x_1, x_2, \ldots, x_n$ can be represented by

$$\begin{pmatrix} 1 & 2 & \cdots & n \\ i_1 & i_2 & \cdots & i_n \end{pmatrix}$$

where $i_1, i_2, \ldots, i_n$ is simply a rearrangement of $1, 2, \ldots, n$. Next let us compute the order of S_n. The order of S_n is the number of ways to map the set $\{1, 2, \ldots, n\}$ onto itself in a one-to-one manner. There are n possible images for 1. After the image of 1 is chosen, there are $n - 1$ possible images for 2, there are $n - 2$ possible images for 3, and so on. Hence the number of permutations of $1, 2, \ldots, n$ is $n(n - 1)(n - 2) \cdots 3 \cdot 2 \cdot 1 = n!$ (n factorial).

Since S_4 has 4! or 24 elements, it would be extremely tedious to list all the elements and display a table for its binary operation. However, since

S_3 has 3! or 6 elements, such an undertaking is feasible. We conclude the discussion of this example by doing just that. The group S_3 is the set $\{\epsilon, \alpha, \beta, \gamma, \delta, \varphi\}$ where

$$\epsilon = \begin{pmatrix} 1 & 2 & 3 \\ 1 & 2 & 3 \end{pmatrix}, \quad \alpha = \begin{pmatrix} 1 & 2 & 3 \\ 2 & 1 & 3 \end{pmatrix}, \quad \beta = \begin{pmatrix} 1 & 2 & 3 \\ 3 & 2 & 1 \end{pmatrix},$$

$$\gamma = \begin{pmatrix} 1 & 2 & 3 \\ 1 & 3 & 2 \end{pmatrix}, \quad \delta = \begin{pmatrix} 1 & 2 & 3 \\ 2 & 3 & 1 \end{pmatrix}, \quad \varphi = \begin{pmatrix} 1 & 2 & 3 \\ 3 & 1 & 2 \end{pmatrix}.$$

Thus,

	ϵ	α	β	γ	δ	φ
ϵ	ϵ	α	β	γ	δ	φ
α	α	ϵ	φ	δ	γ	β
β	β	δ	ϵ	φ	α	γ
γ	γ	φ	δ	ϵ	β	α
δ	δ	β	γ	α	φ	ϵ
φ	φ	γ	α	β	ϵ	δ

Example 6. Consider a rigid square with center 0 and vertices 1, 2, 3, and 4.

We wish to study all rigid motions of the square into itself; i.e., all motions which return the square to the same position although there may be interchange of some of the vertices. Such a motion can be thought of as a permutation of the symbols 1, 2, 3, 4. For instance, let R_0 denote a 90° counterclockwise rotation about the center. This motion sends 1 to 2, 2 to 3, 3 to 4, and 4 to 1. We can denote this rotation R_0 by

$$R_0 = \begin{pmatrix} 1 & 2 & 3 & 4 \\ 2 & 3 & 4 & 1 \end{pmatrix}.$$

To perform a 180° counterclockwise rotation, one applies R_0 twice, i.e.,

$$R_0^2 = \begin{pmatrix} 1 & 2 & 3 & 4 \\ 3 & 4 & 1 & 2 \end{pmatrix}.$$

Hence,

$$R_0^3 = \begin{pmatrix} 1 & 2 & 3 & 4 \\ 4 & 1 & 2 & 3 \end{pmatrix}$$

and

$$R_0^4 = \begin{pmatrix} 1 & 2 & 3 & 4 \\ 1 & 2 & 3 & 4 \end{pmatrix} = E,$$

the "identity" motion.

Let R_1 denote a rotation about the vertical line BD. Then,

$$R_1 = \begin{pmatrix} 1 & 2 & 3 & 4 \\ 2 & 1 & 4 & 3 \end{pmatrix} \quad \text{and} \quad R_1^2 = E.$$

Let R_2 denote a rotation about the horizontal line AC; then

$$R_2 = \begin{pmatrix} 1 & 2 & 3 & 4 \\ 4 & 3 & 2 & 1 \end{pmatrix} \quad \text{and} \quad R_2^2 = E.$$

Let R_3 and R_4 denote rotations about the diagonal lines through 1 and 3 and through 2 and 4 respectively. Then

$$R_3 = \begin{pmatrix} 1 & 2 & 3 & 4 \\ 1 & 4 & 3 & 2 \end{pmatrix} \quad \text{and} \quad R_3^2 = E,$$

and

$$R_4 = \begin{pmatrix} 1 & 2 & 3 & 4 \\ 3 & 2 & 1 & 4 \end{pmatrix} \quad \text{and} \quad R_4^2 = E.$$

Now consider the set

$$T = \{E, R_0, R_0^2, R_0^3, R_1, R_2, R_3, R_4\}.$$

Prove that T is a group with binary operation being composition of mappings (which we know is associative by Lemma 1.2.7). Make a table for this group.

2.3.1 Exercises

1. Prove Theorem 2.2.2, part (ii).

2. If a, b, c are elements of a group G, prove that

$$((a \cdot b) \cdot c)^{-1} = (c^{-1} \cdot b^{-1}) \cdot a^{-1}.$$

3. Prove that a group G is abelian if and only if $(ab)^2 = a^2 b^2$ for all $a, b \in G$.

4. Prove that a group is abelian if $x^2 = e$ for all x in the group.

5. For each of the following sets, determine whether or not it is a group with the indicated operation. If it is a group, what is the identity element, and what are the inverses of each element?

   a) The set $\{0, 2, 4, 6\}$ of $I/(8)$ with operation addition
   b) The set $\{a + b\sqrt{2} \mid a, b \in I\}$ with operation multiplication
   c) The set $\{a + b\sqrt[3]{2} \mid a, b \in I\}$ with operation multiplication
   d) The set N of nonnegative integers with operation addition
   e) The set I of all integers with operation defined by $a \cdot b = a - b$ for all $a, b \in I$
   f) The set I of all integers with operation defined by $a \cdot b = a + b + 1$
   g) The set I of all integers with operation defined by $a \cdot b = a + b - ab$

h) The set $\{a, b, c, d\}$ with operation defined by the following table.

·	a	b	c	d
a	a	b	c	d
b	b	c	d	b
c	c	d	a	b
d	d	a	c	a

i) The set $\{a, b, c, d\}$ with operation defined by the following table.

·	a	b	c	d
a	d	a	b	c
b	a	b	c	d
c	b	c	d	a
d	c	d	a	b

6. Prove parts (2) and (3) of Theorem 2.2.8.

7. Prove that every group which has three, four, or five elements is abelian.

8. Prove that S_3 represents all possible rotations of an equilateral triangle.

9. Consider the group of rotations of the square (Example 6) and the symmetric group S_4. Are they the same group? If not, what is the relationship between these two groups?

In Exercises 8 and 9 above, what would you conjecture about a geometric situation that would produce S_4? Since there must be four vertices, it is natural to guess that all rotations of a tetrahedron would produce S_4. But there is some difficulty in writing it out. Recall that, to obtain S_3 by rotating an equilateral triangle, we had to use three-dimensional space. Hence, to visualize the rotations of the three-dimensional tetrahedron, we must use four-dimensional space.

10. Let Q denote the set of rational numbers. Two rational numbers a/b, c/d $(a, b, c, d \in I, b \neq 0, d \neq 0)$ are said to be *equal* if $ad = bc$. Thus $a/b = ax/bx$ for all nonzero $x \in I$. Hence rational numbers have many representations.

a) The usual addition for rational numbers is

$$\frac{a}{b} + \frac{c}{d} = \frac{ad + bc}{bd}$$

for all $\frac{a}{b}, \frac{c}{d} \in Q$. Prove that this addition is well defined.

b) Define a new addition on Q by

$$\frac{a}{b} \oplus \frac{c}{d} = \frac{a + c}{b + d}$$

for all $\frac{a}{b}, \frac{c}{d} \in Q$. Prove that this addition is not well defined.

11. Let G_1, G_2 be two groups. Define an operation on the Cartesian product $G_1 \times G_2$ such that $G_1 \times G_2$ is a group. Include proofs.

12. Let G be a group of order 4. Prove that, except for renaming elements, G has one of the following group tables.

·	e	a	b	c
e	e	a	b	c
a	a	b	c	e
b	b	c	e	a
c	c	e	a	b

·	e	a	b	c
e	e	a	b	c
a	a	e	c	b
b	b	c	e	a
c	c	b	a	e

2.4 SUBGROUPS

If G is a group, it is possible that there are nonempty subsets of G which are groups themselves with respect to the binary operation defined on G. We say that such subsets are subgroups. More precisely, we make the following definition.

2.4.1 Definition. *A nonempty subset H of a group G is a* **subgroup** *if H is a group with the binary operation of G.*

Note that every group is a subgroup of itself. Moreover, the set consisting of the identity element is a subgroup of every group. Hence every group consisting of more than one element has at least two subgroups. If G is a group with identity element e, then all subgroups of G other than G itself and $\{e\}$ are called *proper* subgroups of G.

To prove that a nonempty subset H of a group G is a subgroup of G, one must verify that H satisfies the axioms G1–G4 of a group. However, since the elements of H are also elements of G, they must satisfy axioms G1–G4 for the group G. We make use of this fact to prove the following theorem, which states that in order to prove that H is a group, it is not necessary to check to see if all four axioms G1–G4 hold.

2.4.2 Theorem. *Let G be a group with binary operation $\cdot$. A nonempty subset H of G is a subgroup of G if and only if*

1) $a \cdot b \in H$ *for all $a, b \in H$, and*
2) *for each $a \in H$, $a^{-1} \in H$.*

Proof. First of all, if H is a subgroup of G, then H is a group itself. Hence (1) and (2) must hold since they are simply G1 and G4 for the group H. Now assume that (1) and (2) hold. We shall prove that H is a subgroup of G by verifying that G1–G4 hold for H. Since (1) and (2) are true by hypothesis, G1 and G4 hold for H. Let a, b, c be arbitrary elements in H. Then a, b, c belong to G, and since G is a group, $a \cdot (b \cdot c) = (a \cdot b) \cdot c$. Hence G2 holds for H. Let g be any element of H. Then (2) guarantees that g^{-1} also belongs to H and (1) implies that $e = g \cdot g^{-1}$ belongs to H where e is the identity element of G. This proves that G3 holds for H. Therefore H is a group and hence is a subgroup of G.

Next we prove a corollary which makes it even easier to prove that a nonempty subset of a group is a subgroup.

2.4.3 Corollary. *Let G be a group with binary operation $\cdot$. A nonempty subset of H is a subgroup of G if and only if*

3) $a^{-1} \cdot b \in H$ *for all $a, b \in H$.*

Proof. Suppose (3) holds. To prove that H is a subgroup of G, we will prove that (1) and (2) of Theorem 2.4.2 hold. Let $a \in H$. Then (3) implies that $a^{-1} \cdot a \in H$. Hence $e \in H$. Thus (3) now implies that $a^{-1} \cdot e = a^{-1} \in H$. Thus (2) holds. Now let $a, b \in H$. Then by (2), $a^{-1}, b \in H$. Now (3) implies that $(a^{-1})^{-1} \cdot b \in H$. However, by Theorem 2.2.4, $(a^{-1})^{-1} = a$. Consequently, for $a, b \in H$, we must have $a \cdot b \in H$. We have thus proved that (1) holds, and therefore H is a subgroup of G.

Now, on the other hand, suppose that H is a subgroup of G. Let $a, b \in H$. By G4, $a^{-1} \in H$, and by G1, $a^{-1} \cdot b \in H$. Hence (3) holds.

Either Theorem 2.4.2 or Corollary 2.4.3 may be employed to prove that a certain nonempty subset of a given group is a subgroup of the group. It should be emphasized that all that is required is to verify that (1) and (2) in Theorem 2.4.2 or (3) in Corollary 2.4.3 are satisfied by the elements of the nonempty subset to prove that the nonempty set is a subgroup.

Consider, as an example, the group S_4. The set T of all rotations of a square (Example 6) is a nonempty subset of S_4 and, in addition, T itself is a group. Thus T is a subgroup of S_4. Now consider the subset $U = \{E, R_0^2, R_1, R_2\}$ of T. We will prove that U is a subgroup of T. (Note that U is also a subgroup of S_4.) To show that U is closed under the binary operation, we exhibit a table.

$\cdot$	E	R_0^2	R_1	R_2
E	E	R_0^2	R_1	R_2
R_0^2	R_0^2	E	R_2	R_1
R_1	R_1	R_2	E	R_0^2
R_2	R_2	R_1	R_0^2	E

Moreover, since each element of U is its own inverse, (1) and (2) of Theorem 2.4.2 are satisfied. Hence U is a subgroup of T.

It should be pointed out that, in general, there is no simple method for finding all subgroups of a given group. One must consider all nonempty subsets, keeping in mind that the subset must be closed under the binary operation of the group and that each element in the subset must have an inverse in the subset. Lagrange's Theorem, which we will prove in

Section 2.5, will simplify somewhat the process of finding all subgroups by eliminating some subsets.

2.4.4 Theorem. *Let G be a group with binary operation* $\cdot$, *and let g be an element of G. Then*

$$H = \{g^i \mid i \text{ is an integer}\}$$

is a subgroup of G.

Proof. Let a, b be arbitrary elements of H. Then $a = g^m$ and $b = g^k$ for some integers m and k. Then $a \cdot b = g^m \cdot g^k = g^{m+k}$ (see Remark 2.2.9). Hence $a \cdot b \in H$. Also $g^{-m} \in H$ and $a \cdot g^{-m} = g^m \cdot g^{-m} = g^{m-m} = e$, by Definition 2.2.7. Similarly $g^{-m} \cdot a = g^{-m} \cdot g^m = e$. Hence g^{-m} is the inverse of a; i.e., $a^{-1} = g^{-m} \in H$. Thus (1) and (2) of Theorem 2.4.2 hold. Therefore H is a subgroup.

There is a special name for groups of this type.

2.4.5 Definition. *A group H is said to be **cyclic** if there exists an element* $g \in H$ *such that every element of H can be written as* g^n *for some integer* n. *In this case, H is called the **cyclic group generated by g**, and g is called a **generator** of H. If H is a subgroup of another group G, then H is called a **cyclic subgroup.***

The subset $V = \{E, R_0, R_0^2, R_0^3\}$ of the group T of rotations of the square is a subgroup (as is easily checked) and, in fact, is cyclic. The group V can be generated by either R_0 or R_0^3. That R_0 generates V is evident; to see that R_0^3 also generates V, observe that

$$(R_0^3)^1 = R_0^3,$$
$$(R_0^3)^2 = R_0^6 = R_0^4 \cdot R_0^2 = R_0^2,$$
$$(R_0^3)^3 = R_0^9 = R_0^8 \cdot R_0 = R_0,$$

and

$$(R_0^3)^4 = R_0^{12} = (R_0^4)^3 = E.$$

On the other hand, the elements R_1, R_2, R_3, and R_4 of T generate cyclic subgroups of order 2.

Also, for any positive integer n, the group $I/(n)$ of integers modulo n is cyclic. For example, consider $I/(5)$. Here the binary operation is addition; consequently, if $[x]$ is an element of $I/(5)$, then $[x]^i$ means to add $[x]$ to itself i times. Hence, when addition is the binary operation, it is customary to write $i[x]$ instead of $[x]^i$. Though $[1]$ is the most obvious choice of generator for $I/(5)$, it is true in this case that every nonzero element of $I/(5)$ will generate the entire group. Check it! What elements of $I/(6)$ will generate the entire group? What would you conjecture about the generators of $I/(n)$ for an arbitrary positive integer n?

Next we determine the elements in a *finite* cyclic group.

2.4.6 Theorem. *Let G be a finite cyclic group generated by g. If $o(G) = n$, then $g^n = e$ and*

$$\{g, g^2, \ldots, g^{n-1}, g^n = e\}$$

is precisely the set of elements belonging to G.

Proof. First we show that $g^m \neq e$ for any positive integer $m < n$. Suppose this is not the case; that is, suppose $g^m = e$ for some positive integer $m < n$. Let $x \in G$. Then, since G is a cyclic group generated by g, $x = g^k$ for some integer k. Then by the uniqueness part of the division algorithm for the integers (Lemma 1.6.1), there exist unique integers q, r such that $k = qm + r$ and $0 \leq r < m$. Then

$$x = g^k = g^{qm+r} = (g^m)^q \cdot g^r = e^q \cdot g^r = e \cdot g^r = g^r.$$

Hence every element of G is of the form g^r where $0 \leq r < m$. Hence G has at most m elements where $m < n$. But by hypothesis, G has exactly n elements, so we have a contradiction, and hence $g^m \neq e$ for any positive integer $m < n$.

We know that the elements $g, g^2, \ldots, g^{n-1}, g^n$ all belong to G. Next we show that these elements are distinct. Suppose that $g^i = g^j$ for some positive integers i and j with $i < j \leq n$. Then, multiplying by g^{-i}, we get

$$e = g^0 = g^{i-i} = g^i \cdot g^{-i} = g^j \cdot g^{-i} = g^{j-i}$$

and since $i < j \leq n$, we must have $0 < j - i < n$. But the first paragraph of this proof showed that $a^m \neq e$ for $m < n$. Hence $g^{j-i} \neq e$, which is a contradiction. Thus the elements $g, g^2, \ldots, g^{n-1}, g^n$ are all distinct.

Since $o(G) = n$, then G must be precisely the set

$$\{g, g^2, \ldots, g^{n-1}, g^n\}.$$

However, since G is a group, e must belong to G. But $g^m \neq e$ if $m < n$. Hence g^n must equal e. This completes the proof of the theorem.

Let us restate the result of this theorem in the following form.

2.4.7 Corollary. *If G is a finite cyclic group generated by g and of order n, then n is the least positive integer such that $g^n = e$.*

Now we are ready to make the following definition.

2.4.8 Definition. *Let g be an element of a group G.*

1) *If there exists a positive integer m such that $g^m = e$, then the smallest such positive integer is the **order of g**. In this case, g has **finite order**.*

2) *If no such integer exists, we say g has **infinite order**.*

We will use the symbol $o(g)$ to denote the order of the element g of G. This should not be confused with the symbol $o(G)$, which denotes the order of the group G.

2.4.9 Remark. Notice that Corollary 2.4.7 states that if the cyclic group generated by an element g has order n, then $o(g) = n$. On the other hand, if $o(g) = n$, then, as was shown in the proof of Theorem 2.4.6, $\{g, g^2, \ldots, g^{n-1}, g^n = e\}$ are all distinct. Hence the cyclic group generated by g has order n. Consequently, the order of an element is simply the order of the cyclic group it generates.

The next theorem and corollary tell precisely what the subgroups of a cyclic group are like.

2.4.10 Theorem. *Every subgroup of a cyclic group is cyclic.*

Proof. Let H be a subgroup of a cyclic group G. Let g be the generator of G. If $H = \{e\}$, then H is certainly cyclic with generator e. Hence assume that $H \neq \{e\}$. Since H is a subgroup of G, every element of H is of the form g^k for some integer k. Let m be the least positive integer such that $g^m \in H$. Let g^k be an arbitrary element of H. By the division algorithm for the integers (Lemma 1.6.1), there exist integers q, r such that $k = mq + r$ and $0 \leq r < m$. Then $r = k - mq$, and hence

$$g^r = g^{k+(-mq)} = g^k \cdot g^{-mq} = g^k \cdot (g^m)^{-q}.$$

Since $g^m \in H$, then $(g^m)^{-q}$ must also be in H. Moreover, since $g^k \in H$, then $g^k \cdot (g^m)^{-q}$ must be in H. Hence $g^r \in H$. Now suppose $r \neq 0$; then $0 < r < m$. But since m was chosen to be the least positive integer such that $g^m \in H$, and since $g^r \in H$ with $0 < r < m$, we must have a contradiction. Therefore $r = 0$ and hence $k = mq$. We have shown that an arbitrary element k^k of H is of the form $(g^m)^q$; i.e., H is a cyclic group with generator g^m. This completes the proof.

In proving Theorem 2.4.10, we actually proved the following result, which is more specific about the subgroups of a finite cyclic group.

2.4.11 Corollary. *If a finite cyclic group G has order n and is generated by g, then the subgroups of G are precisely the subgroups generated by g^m where m divides n.*

Proof. By Theorem 2.4.10, we know all of this except that m must divide n. Let H be a subgroup of G. Since $o(G) = n$, we know by Theorem 2.4.6 that $g^n = e$. Hence $g^n \in H$. Now apply the division algorithm, as in the proof of Theorem 2.4.10, using g^n in place of g^k. Thus we see that $n = mq$, and so m divides n, as asserted.

2.4.12 Exercises

1. Prove or disprove that the following sets are subgroups of the corresponding group.

   a) Is the set of all multiples of 6 a subgroup of the group of integers with addition as binary operation?

b) Is $\{\epsilon, \alpha\}$ a subgroup of the group discussed in Example 5, Section 2.3?
c) Is $\{3, 6, 9\}$ a subgroup of $I/(10)$ with addition as binary operation?
d) Is the set of matrices of the form

$$\begin{pmatrix} a & b \\ 0 & 0 \end{pmatrix}$$

where a, b are integers, a subgroup of the group in Example 3, Section 2.3?

2. Find all subgroups of the following groups.

a) $I/(8)$ with addition as binary operation.
b) $I/(7)$ with addition as binary operation.
c) The group of rotations of a square; Example 6, Section 2.3. (There are 10 of them.)
d) S_3, the group of permutations of 3 symbols; Example 5, Section 2.3.

3. Let G be a group, and let A and B be subgroups of G. Prove that $A \cap B$ is a subgroup of G. Show that $A \cup B$ need not be a subgroup of G.

4. Let G be an abelian group, and let A and B be subgroups of G. Denote by $A \cdot B$ the set $\{a \cdot b \mid a \in A, b \in B\}$. Prove that $A \cdot B$ is a subgroup of G.

5. Prove that every cyclic group is abelian. By counterexample, show that the converse is not true.

6. Let G be a cyclic group of order 24 and generator g. List *all* subgroups of G.

2.5 COSETS AND LAGRANGE'S THEOREM

In this section we will study more closely the relationship between a group and its subgroups. In particular, we use a subgroup of a group to perform a decomposition of the group, and we prove the important Theorem of Lagrange, which states that only certain subsets of a group are eligible to be subgroups. The concept of *cosets* is extremely important in the study of modern algebra in general and is not merely a group theoretic notion. This section deserves special attention since the results obtained here will be used throughout the study of algebraic systems.

2.5.1 Definition. *Let G be a group and let H be a subgroup of G. If g is an arbitrary element of G, then*

$$gH = \{g \cdot h \mid h \in H\}$$

*is called the **left coset of H in G determined by g**. The element g is often called a **representative** of the left coset gH.*

Similarly, $Hg = \{h \cdot g \mid h \in H\}$ is called the right coset of H in G determined by g. Of course, if G is abelian, $Hg = gH$ for all $g \in G$. We will consider only left cosets here; however, with minor alterations, the discussion in this section could be repeated for right cosets. Note that if e is the identity element of G, then $eH = H$ so that H itself is a left coset of H in G.

As we will see, the set of all left cosets of a subgroup H in a group G decomposes G into disjoint subsets. Before proceeding with the proof of this, let us consider an example.

In Section 2.3, we defined the group S_3 of permutations on 3 symbols. The elements of S_3 are the following:

$$\epsilon = \begin{pmatrix} 1 & 2 & 3 \\ 1 & 2 & 3 \end{pmatrix}, \quad \alpha = \begin{pmatrix} 1 & 2 & 3 \\ 2 & 1 & 3 \end{pmatrix}, \quad \beta = \begin{pmatrix} 1 & 2 & 3 \\ 3 & 2 & 1 \end{pmatrix},$$

$$\gamma = \begin{pmatrix} 1 & 2 & 3 \\ 1 & 3 & 2 \end{pmatrix}, \quad \delta = \begin{pmatrix} 1 & 2 & 3 \\ 2 & 3 & 1 \end{pmatrix} \quad \varphi = \begin{pmatrix} 1 & 2 & 3 \\ 3 & 1 & 2 \end{pmatrix}.$$

Let $H = \{\epsilon, \alpha\}$. Then H is a subgroup of S_3. We will compute all the left cosets of H in S_3.

$$\epsilon H = \alpha H = \{\epsilon, \alpha\},$$
$$\beta H = \delta H = \{\beta, \delta\},$$
$$\gamma H = \varphi H = \{\gamma, \varphi\}.$$

(Check these computations as an exercise.) Hence there are three distinct left cosets of H in S_3. Observe that, in fact, these distinct left cosets form a partition of S_3. We will soon see that this is always the case. Also notice that the order of S_3 is the product of the order of H and the number of distinct left cosets of H in S_3.

In Section 1.4 we studied equivalence relations. One important property of equivalence relations that we proved (Theorem 1.4.4) is that the set of equivalence classes forms a partition. Consequently, one should ask if the partition of S_3 by the left cosets of H in S_3 could have been accomplished by an equivalence relation. If so, will this process work in the general case? We answer these questions affirmatively in this section.

2.5.2 Definition. *Let G be a group and H a subgroup of G. For any two elements a, b $\in$ G, say **a is congruent to b modulo H**, and write*

$$a \equiv b \ (mod \ H),$$

if $b^{-1} \cdot a \in H$.

Thus "congruence modulo H" is a relation on the set G. Here we write $a \equiv b \pmod{H}$ in place of $a \sim b$, which was the symbol for relation in Section 1.4.

2.5.3 Theorem. *The relation defined above is an equivalence relation.*

Proof. We must verify that the reflexive, symmetric, and transitive properties hold. The details are left as an exercise.

2.5.4 Theorem. *Let G be a group with subgroup H. Let a $\in$ G and let [a] denote the equivalence class of a with regard to the equivalence relation a $\equiv$ b (mod H) for all a, b $\in$ G; that is, [a] = $\{x \in G \mid x \equiv a \ (mod \ H)\}$.*

Then $[a] = aH;$

that is, the equivalence class of a is precisely the left coset of H in G determined by a.

Proof. $[a] = \{x \in G \mid x \equiv a \pmod{H}\}$
$= \{x \in G \mid a^{-1} \cdot x = h \text{ for some } h \in H\}$
$= \{x \in G \mid x = a \cdot h \text{ for some } h \in H\}$
$= aH.$

If one uses right cosets instead of left cosets, one must define $a \equiv b$ (mod H) if $a \cdot b^{-1} \in H$ for all $a, b \in G$. Then the equivalence class of $[a]$ is the right coset Ha.

Since the set of left cosets of H in G are simply the equivalence classes of an equivalence relation on the set G, Theorem 1.4.4 immediately gives us the following theorem.

2.5.5 Theorem. *Let G be a group and Let H be a subgroup of G. Then the set of left cosets of H in G form a partition of G. Hence every element of G belongs to one and only one left coset of G in H.*

Now we are ready to state and prove the important theorem attributed to the French mathematician Joseph Louis Lagrange (1736–1813).

2.5.6 Theorem (Lagrange). *The order of a subgroup of a finite group divides the order of the group.*

Proof. Let G be a finite group, say $o(G) = n$. Let H be a subgroup of G. Then H is finite, say $o(H) = m$. Let k be the number of left cosets of H in G.

First we show that there is a one-to-one correspondence between any two left cosets of H in G; that is, given two arbitrary left cosets of H in G, say aH and bH where $a, b \in G$, there exists a one-to-one mapping from aH onto bH. Define a mapping $\alpha: aH \rightarrow bH$ by $\alpha(ah) = bh$ for all $h \in H$. Then α is onto since for each $bh \in bH$, there exists $ah \in aH$ such that $\alpha(ah) = bh$. Now let $ah, ah_1 \in aH, ah \neq ah_1$. Suppose $\alpha(ah) = \alpha(ah_1)$; that is $bh = bh_1$. Then, by the cancellation law, $h = h_1$, and so $ah = ah_1$, a contradiction. Hence $\alpha(ah) \neq \alpha(ah_1)$, and therefore α is one-to-one.

Hence each left coset of H in G has the same number of elements. Moreover, since H itself is a left coset, each left coset contains the same number of elements as H; i.e., the number of elements in each left coset is $o(H) = m$. By Theorem 2.5.5, the set of left cosets form a partition of G. Consequently each element of G lies in exactly one of the k left cosets of H in G. Since each coset has exactly m elements, G must have mk elements. Thus $o(G) = n = mk = o(H)k$. Hence $o(H)$ divides $o(G)$, and the theorem is proved.

Lagrange's Theorem has several corollaries which are important in their own right. We list a few.

2.5.7 Corollary. *If G is a finite group of order n, then $g^n = e$ for all $g \in G$.*

Proof. Let g be an element of G. Then $H = \{g^i \mid i \text{ is an integer}\}$ is a subgroup of G (Theorem 2.4.4); i.e., H is the cyclic subgroup generated by g. By Lagrange's Theorem, $o(H)$ divides $o(G) = n$. Hence, if $o(H) = m$, then $n = mk$ for some positive integer k. By Theorem 2.4.6, $g^m = e$. Hence

$$g^n = g^{mk} = (g^m)^k = e^k = e,$$

which proves the corollary.

2.5.8 Corollary. *The order of every element of a finite group is a divisor of the order of the group.*

Proof. The order of every element of a finite group is the order of the cyclic subgroup it generates, and the order of this subgroup divides the order of the group.

2.5.9 Corollary. *If G is a finite group of order p where p is a prime integer, then G is cyclic and every element of G except the identity is a generator of G.*

Proof. By Corollary 2.5.8, the order of every element of G except the identity is p since p has no divisors other than p and 1. Hence the cyclic subgroup generated by any element of G other than the identity has order p and therefore must be all of G.

2.5.10 Definition. *Let G be a finite group and let H be a subgroup of G. The number of left cosets of H in G is the **index of H in G**. The symbol $i_G(H)$ denotes the index of H in G.*

By Lagrange's Theorem, if G is a finite group and H is a subgroup of G, then

$$i_G(H) = \frac{o(G)}{o(H)}.$$

2.5.11 Exercises

1. Prove Theorem 2.5.3.
2. Let G be a finite group, and let H_1, H_2 be subgroups of G of orders p, q respectively, where p, q are distinct prime integers. Prove that $H_1 \cap H_2 = \{e\}$.

2.6 NORMAL SUBGROUPS AND FACTOR GROUPS

In this section we consider a special and extremely important collection of subgroups—namely normal subgroups. The word "normal" here is misleading, as we will see; in fact, normal subgroups are very special and constitute a relatively small class of subgroups. Given a group G and a normal subgroup H of G, we will construct another group related to G and H which will be called the factor group.

2.6.1 Definition. *A subgroup H of a group G is a **normal subgroup** of G if for all $g \in G$ and for all $h \in H$, $(g \cdot h) \cdot g^{-1} \in H$.*

2.6.2 Theorem. *Let H be a subgroup of a group G. The following are equivalent.*

1) *H is a normal subgroup of G.*
2) *$Ha = aH$ for all $a \in G$; that is, every right coset is also a left coset and vice versa.*
3) *$aH \cdot bH = (a \cdot b)H$ for all a, $b \in H$; that is, the product of left cosets is also a left coset.*

Proof. We will prove that (1) implies (2), (2) implies (3), and (3) implies (1). Note that $Ha = aH$ does not mean that $ha = ah$ for all $h \in H$. The equality $Ha = aH$ simply means that these two sets Ha and aH are the same. Hence, if $Ha = aH$, then for any $h \in H$, there exists $h_1 \in H$ such that $ha = ah_1$. Also $(a \cdot b)H$ denotes the left coset of H in G determined by the element $a \cdot b$ of G.

(1) *implies* (2). Assume that H is a normal subgroup of G. Let $a \in G$. An arbitrary element of aH is ah where $h \in H$. Since, H is a normal subgroup of G, $(a \cdot h) \cdot a^{-1} \in H$; that is, $(a \cdot h) \cdot a^{-1} = h_1$ for some $h_1 \in H$. Then

$$a \cdot h = (a \cdot h) \cdot (a^{-1} \cdot a) = h_1 \cdot a \in Ha$$

since $h_1 \in H$. Thus $aH \subseteq Ha$. Now pick an arbitrary element $h_2 \cdot a \in Ha$; $h_2 \in H$. Since $a \in G$, $a^{-1} \in G$. Thus, since H is a normal subgroup of G,

$$(a^{-1} \cdot h_2) \cdot (a^{-1})^{-1} = (a^{-1} \cdot h_2) \cdot a \in H.$$

Hence $a^{-1} \cdot (h_2 \cdot a) = h_3$ for some $h_3 \in H$. Then

$$h_2 \cdot a = (a \cdot a^{-1}) \cdot (h_2 \cdot a) = a \cdot h_3 \in aH.$$

Hence $Ha \subseteq aH$, and finally $Ha = aH$.

(2) *implies* (3). Assume that $aH = Ha$ for all $a \in G$, Let

$$x = (a \cdot h) \cdot (b \cdot h_1) = a \cdot (h \cdot b) \cdot h_1$$

be an arbitrary element of $aH \cdot bH$; that is, h, $h_1 \in H$ and a, $b \in G$. Since $bH = Hb$, there exists $h_2 \in H$ such that $b \cdot h_2 = h \cdot b$. Hence

$$x = a \cdot (b \cdot h_2) \cdot h_1 = (a \cdot b) \cdot (h_2 \cdot h_1) \in (a \cdot b)H$$

since h_2, $h_1 \in H$. Therefore

$$aH \cdot bH \subseteq (a \cdot b)H.$$

Now let $y = (a \cdot b) \cdot h_1$ be an arbitrary element of $(a \cdot b)H$; that is, $a, b \in G$ and $h_1 \in H$. For any $h \in H$,

$$y = (a \cdot b) \cdot h_1 = \big((a \cdot (h \cdot h^{-1}) \cdot b) \cdot h_1\big) = \big((a \cdot h) \cdot (h^{-1} \cdot b)\big) \cdot h_1.$$

But since $bH = Hb$, there exists $h_2 \in H$ such that $h^{-1} \cdot b = b \cdot h_2$. Hence

$$y = (a \cdot h) \cdot \big((b \cdot h_2) \cdot h_1\big) = (a \cdot h) \cdot (b \cdot h_3)$$

for $h_3 = h_2 \cdot h_1 \in H$. Hence $y \in aH \cdot bH$, and thus $(a \cdot b)H \subseteq aH \cdot bH$. Consequently $aH \cdot bH = (a \cdot b)H$.

(3) implies (1). Assume that $aH \cdot bH = (a \cdot b)H$ for $a, b \in G$. Then for any $a \in G$,

$$aH \cdot (a^{-1}H) = (a \cdot a^{-1})H = eH = H.$$

Hence, for $h \in H$, $(a \cdot h) \cdot (a^{-1} \cdot h_1) = h_2$ for some $h_1, h_2 \in H$. Then

$$(a \cdot h) \cdot a^{-1} = \big((a \cdot h) \cdot a^{-1}\big) \cdot (h_1 \cdot h_1^{-1}) = h_2 \cdot h_1^{-1} \in H.$$

Thus H is a normal subgroup of G.

In Section 2.5 we computed the left cosets of the subgroup $H = \{\epsilon, \alpha\}$ in S_3. The distinct left cosets of H in S_3 are H, βH, and γH. Now let us compute the right cosets of H in S_3:

$$H\epsilon = H\alpha = \{\epsilon, \alpha\}, \qquad H\beta = H\varphi = \{\beta, \varphi\}, \qquad H\gamma = H\delta = \{\gamma, \delta\}.$$

By comparing the left and right cosets of H in G, one sees that H is not a normal subgroup of S_3. On the other hand, if $N = \{\epsilon, \delta, \varphi\}$, then N is a subgroup of S_3 and, in fact, N is a normal subgroup of S_3 since the left cosets of N in S_3 are

$$\epsilon N = \delta N = \varphi N = \{\epsilon, \delta, \varphi\} \qquad \text{and} \qquad \alpha N = \beta N = \gamma N = \{\alpha, \beta, \gamma\},$$

whereas the right cosets of N in G are

$$N\epsilon = N\delta = N\varphi = \{\epsilon, \delta, \varphi\} \qquad \text{and} \qquad N\alpha = N\beta = N\gamma = \{\alpha, \beta, \gamma\}.$$

It is property (3) of Theorem 2.6.2 that makes normal subgroups important. It is a tribute to the genius of the French mathematician Evariste Galois (1811–1832) that he recognized that those groups whose left cosets were also right cosets were special. Using property (3) he was able to define a binary operation on the set of all left cosets of a subgroup in the group. Hence he formed a new group whose elements are cosets.

Let G be a group and let H be a normal subgroup of G. Let G/H be the set of all left cosets of H in G. Define an operation on G/H by

$$aH \cdot bH = (a \cdot b)H \qquad \text{for all } aH, bH \in G/H.$$

We want to prove that this is a binary operation on G/H. By the equivalence of parts (1) and (3) of Theorem 2.6.2, we know that the product of two elements of G/H is also an element of G/H.

However, the multiplication defined in G/H depends on the representatives picked for each left coset; that is, the product of a coset represented by a and a coset represented by b is a coset represented by $a \cdot b$. What if different representatives were picked? For instance, suppose $aH = a_1 H$ and $bH = b_1 H$. Then

$$aH \cdot bH = (a \cdot b)H \qquad \text{and} \qquad a_1 H \cdot b_1 H = (a_1 \cdot b_1)H.$$

Is $(a \cdot b)H = (a_1 \cdot b_1)H$? We must prove that $(a \cdot b)H = (a_1 \cdot b_1)H$ in order to prove that the multiplication is a binary operation. In doing so, we will be verifying the "uniqueness" part of the definition of binary operation and proving that the multiplication is *well defined*.

Suppose $aH = a_1 H$ and $bH = b_1 H$ for a, a_1, b, $b_1 \in G$. Then, since these left cosets are equivalence classes for the equivalence relation $a \equiv b$ (mod H) if $b^{-1} \cdot a \in H$, we know that

$$a \equiv a_1 \text{ (mod } H) \qquad \text{and} \qquad b \equiv b_1 \text{ (mod } H).$$

Hence $a_1^{-1} \cdot a \in H$ and $b_1^{-1} \cdot b \in H$; that is, $a_1^{-1} \cdot a = h$ and $b_1^{-1} \cdot b = h_1$ for some h, $h_1 \in H$. Then

$$a = (a_1 \cdot a_1^{-1}) \cdot a = a_1 \cdot h \qquad \text{and} \qquad b = b_1 \cdot h_1.$$

This implies that

$$a \cdot b = (a_1 \cdot h) \cdot (b_1 \cdot h_1) = a_1 \cdot \big((h \cdot b_1) \cdot h_1\big).$$

Since H is a normal subgroup of G, $b_1 H = H b_1$. Thus there exists $h_2 \in H$ such that $b_1 \cdot h_2 = h \cdot b_1$. Consequently

$$a \cdot b = a_1 \cdot \big((b_1 \cdot h_2) \cdot h_1\big) = (a_1 \cdot b_1) \cdot (h_2 \cdot h_1) \in (a_1 \cdot b_1)H$$

since $h_2 \cdot h_1 \in H$. Hence $a \cdot b \in [a_1 \cdot b_1]$ so that

$$(a \cdot b)H = [a \cdot b] = [a_1 \cdot b_1] = (a_1 \cdot b_1)H.$$

This proves that the multiplication on G/H is well defined; i.e., multiplication is a binary operation on G/H.

2.6.3 Theorem. *Let G be a group and let H be a normal subgroup of G. Let G/H be the set of all left cosets of H in G and define*

$$aH \cdot bH = (a \cdot b)H \text{ for all } aH, bH \in G/H.$$

Then G/H is a group with this binary operation.

Proof. We have already verified that the multiplication in G/H is a binary operation on G/H; thus G/H is closed and G1 holds. Now let aH, bH,

$cH \in G/H$; i.e., $a, b, c \in G$. Then

$$
\begin{aligned}
(aH \cdot bH) \cdot cH &= (a \cdot b)H \cdot cH \\
&= ((a \cdot b) \cdot c)H \\
&= (a \cdot (b \cdot c))H \qquad \text{(since } G \text{ is associative)} \\
&= aH \cdot (b \cdot c)H \\
&= aH \cdot (bH \cdot cH).
\end{aligned}
$$

Hence the multiplication of G/H is associative, and so G2 holds. $H = eH \in G/H$ and for all $aH \in G/H$,

$$H \cdot aH = (e \cdot a)H = aH$$

and

$$aH \cdot H = (a \cdot e)H = aH.$$

Hence H is the identity of G/H, and so G3 holds. Let $aH \in G/H$. Since G is a group, $a^{-1} \in G$, and so $a^{-1}H \in G/H$. Then

$$aH \cdot a^{-1}H = (a \cdot a^{-1})H = eH = H$$

and

$$a^{-1}H \cdot aH = (a^{-1} \cdot a)H = eH = H.$$

Thus the inverse of aH is $a^{-1}H$. Hence G4 holds, and we have proved that G/H is a group.

2.6.4 Definition. *If G is a group and H is a normal subgroup of G, then the group G/H is called the **factor group of G by H**.*

2.6.5 Theorem. *Let G be a finite group and let H be a normal subgroup of G. Then G/H is a finite group and*

$$o(G/H) = \frac{o(G)}{o(H)}.$$

Proof. The elements of G/H are precisely the left cosets of G in H. Hence $o(G/H)$ is the index of H in G (Definition 2.5.10). Hence

$$o(G/H) = i_G(H) = \frac{o(G)}{o(H)}.$$

We have shown previously that $N = \{\epsilon, \delta, \varphi\}$ is a normal subgroup of S_3. Then it is possible to form the factor group $S_3/N = \{N, \alpha N\}$. Its multiplication table is as follows.

$\cdot$	N	αN
N	N	αN
αN	αN	N

Next let us consider an example of a somewhat different type. Let I be the group of integers with addition as binary operation. Let M be the set of all multiples of 4; i.e., $M = \{4m \mid m \in I\}$. It is a routine matter to check that M is a subgroup of I. However, since the operation in I is addition, the left cosets of M in I are written as $a + M$ rather than aM. Next observe that the left cosets of M in I are precisely M, $1 + M$, $2 + M$, and $3 + M$; for if $n \in I$, by Lemma 1.6.1, there exist q, $r \in I$ such that $n = 4q + r$ and $0 \le r < 4$. Hence $n = r + 4q \in r + M$ where $r = 0, 1, 2,$ or 3. Furthermore, since I is an abelian group,

$$r + M = \{r + m \mid m \in M\} = \{m + r \mid m \in M\} = M + r.$$

Hence all left cosets of M in I are also right cosets of M in I. Thus M is a normal subgroup of I. Therefore it is possible to form the factor group I/M.

Hence $I/M = \{M, 1 + M, 2 + M, 3 + M\}$, and the table for the binary operation in I/M follows.

$+$	M	$1 + M$	$2 + M$	$3 + M$
M	M	$1 + M$	$2 + M$	$3 + M$
$1 + M$	$1 + M$	$2 + M$	$3 + M$	M
$2 + M$	$2 + M$	$3 + M$	M	$1 + M$
$3 + M$	$3 + M$	M	$1 + M$	$2 + M$

The two examples of factor groups discussed here have finite order. However, this is not always the case. It is quite possible to have a factor group of infinite order. For instance, the factor group I/K where I is the group of integers and $K = \{0\}$ has infinite order.

In conclusion, it should be emphasized that the construction of a factor group G/H requires H to be a normal subgroup of G. The factor group G/H plays an extremely important role in the theory of groups. Unfortunately, the use of the factor group in its place in group theory lies beyond the scope of this course. But the distinguishing characteristic of normal subgroups is the fact that being a normal subgroup of a group G allows the construction of the factor group of G.

2.6.6 Exercises

Let G be a group.

1. Given that H is a subgroup of G such that $i_G(H) = 2$, prove that H is a normal subgroup of G.

2. Show that the intersection of two normal subgroups of G is a normal subgroup of G.

3. Show that if H is a normal subgroup of G and K is any subgroup of G, then $H \cap K$ is a normal subgroup of K.

4. For any subgroups H, K of G, we define $HK = \{h \cdot k \mid h \in H, k \in K\}$.

   a) Show that if either H or K is a normal subgroup of G, then HK is a subgroup of G.

b) Show that if both H and K are normal subgroups of G, then HK is a normal subgroup of G.

c) Show that if H and K are arbitrary subgroups of G, then HK need not be a subgroup of G.

5. Let H be a subgroup of G, and for $g \in G$, define $gHg^{-1} = \{(g \cdot h) \cdot g^{-1} \mid h \in H\}$. Prove that gHg^{-1} is a subgroup of G.

6. Show that every subgroup of an abelian group is normal.

7. Let H be a subgroup of G, and define $N(H)$ by $N(H) = \{g \in G \mid gHg^{-1} = H\}$. Then $N(H)$ is called the *normalizer* of H.

   a) Prove that $N(H)$ is a subgroup of G.
   b) Prove that H is a normal subgroup of $N(H)$.
   c) Prove that $N(H)$ is the largest subgroup of G satisfying (b); i.e., prove that if K is a subgroup of G such that H is a normal subgroup of K, then $K \subseteq N(H)$.

2.7 HOMOMORPHISMS AND ISOMORPHISMS

A group is a nonempty set on which there is defined a binary operation which satisfies axioms G1–G4. Since a group consists of more than a nonempty set, we should not be surprised that "meaningful" mappings from one group to another should also be more than just mappings. In fact, there should be some interaction between the mapping and the binary operations on the groups. In this section we focus our attention on such mappings from one group to another.

2.7.1 Definition. *Let G and H be groups with binary operations $\cdot$ and $*$ respectively. A **homomorphism** from G to H is a mapping α from G to H such that*

(1)
$$\alpha(g_1 \cdot g_2) = \alpha(g_1) * \alpha(g_2)$$

for all $g_1, g_2 \in G$.

Let us examine condition (1). For elements g_1 and g_2 in G, $g_1 \cdot g_2$ is also in G. Moreover, $\alpha(g_1)$, $\alpha(g_2)$, and $\alpha(g_1 \cdot g_2)$ belong to H. Condition (1) states that the result is the same whether we combine g_1 and g_2 in G first and then apply the mapping α, or whether we apply the mapping α to g_1 and g_2 separately and then combine $\alpha(g_1)$ and $\alpha(g_2)$ in H (Fig. 2.1). This property of the homomorphism α is often described by saying "α preserves the binary operations of G and H."

A simple example of a homomorphism can be seen by letting G be the cyclic group of order 8 generated by g and letting H be the group of integers modulo 4; i.e.,

$$G = \{e, g, g^2, \ldots, g^7\} \quad \text{and} \quad H = \{0, 1, 2, 3\};$$

by letting the binary operation on G be multiplication and on H, addition;

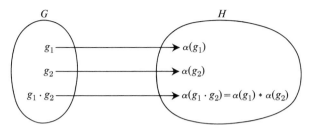

Figure 2.1

and by defining a mapping α from G to H by

$$\alpha(e) = 0, \qquad \alpha(g) = 1, \qquad \alpha(g^2) = 2, \qquad \alpha(g^3) = 3,$$
$$\alpha(g^4) = 0, \qquad \alpha(g^5) = 1, \qquad \alpha(g^6) = 2, \qquad \alpha(g^7) = 3.$$

That α is a homomorphism can be verified by checking all possible pairs of elements of G to see that condition (1) of the definition of homomorphism holds; i.e., one must verify that $\alpha(g^m \cdot g^k) = \alpha(g^m) + \alpha(g^k)$ for all g^m, $g^k \in G$. To illustrate, one case is verified here:

$$\alpha(g^2 \cdot g^5) = \alpha(g^7) = 3 \qquad \text{and} \qquad \alpha(g^2) + \alpha(g^5) = 2 + 1 = 3.$$

Another example of a homomorphism is provided by the logarithm function (with any fixed base). In 2.1.3, Example (4), we showed that the set L of nonzero rational numbers is a group under multiplication. Also in 2.1.3, Example (5), we mentioned that the set R of all real numbers is a group under addition. The function "$log_{10}\,|\,\,|$" is a mapping from L to R such that, for all $x \in L$, $log_{10}\,|x|$ means the logarithm to the base ten of the absolute value of x. It is a well-known property of logarithms that for any $x, y \in L$,

$$log_{10}\,|xy| = log_{10}\,|x| + log_{10}\,|y|.$$

Hence $log_{10}\,|\,\,|$ is a homomorphism from L to R.

2.7.2 Definition. *Let G and H be groups with binary operations $\cdot$ and $*$ respectively. Let α be a homomorphism from G to H. Then*

1) $Im(\alpha) = \{h \in H \mid \alpha(g) = h \text{ for some } g \in G\}$ *is called the **image set** under α, and*

2) $Ker(\alpha) = \{g \in G \mid \alpha(g) = e\}$, *where e is the identity of H is called the **kernel** of α.*

2.7.3 Theorem. *Let G and H be groups with binary operations $\cdot$ and $*$ respectively. Let e_G and e_H be their identity elements. Let α be a homomorphism from G into H. Then*

1) $\alpha(e_G) = e_H$,

2) *for all $g \in G$, $\alpha(g^{-1}) = (\alpha(g))^{-1}$, and*

3) $Ker(\alpha)$ *is a subgroup of G.*

Proof

1) Let $g \in G$. Then $g = g \cdot e_G$. Now, applying the homomorphism α, we get

$$\alpha(g) = \alpha(g \cdot e_G) = \alpha(g) * \alpha(e_G).$$

However, since e_H is the identity in H, $\alpha(g) = \alpha(g) * e_H$. Thus

$$\alpha(g) * \alpha(e_G) = \alpha(g) * e_H.$$

Hence, by the cancellation law, $\alpha(e_G) = e_H$.

2) Let $g \in G$. We are to prove that the image of g^{-1} is the inverse of $\alpha(g)$. Since G is a group, $e_G = g^{-1} \cdot g = g \cdot g^{-1}$. Now apply the homomorphism α:

$$e_H = \alpha(e_G) = \alpha(g^{-1} \cdot g) = \alpha(g^{-1}) * \alpha(g)$$

and

$$e_H = \alpha(e_G) = \alpha(g \cdot g^{-1}) = \alpha(g) * \alpha(g^{-1}).$$

Hence $\alpha(g^{-1})$ is the inverse of $\alpha(g)$ in H, and therefore $\alpha(g^{-1}) = (\alpha(g))^{-1}$.

3) Let g_1, $g_2 \in Ker(\alpha)$. Then, by definition of $Ker(\alpha)$, $\alpha(g_1) = e_H$ and $\alpha(g_2) = e_H$. Consequently,

$$\alpha(g_1 \cdot g_2^{-1}) = \alpha(g_1) * \alpha(g_2^{-1}) = e_H * \alpha(g_2)^{-1} = e_H^{-1} = e_H.$$

Hence $g_1 \cdot g_2^{-1} \in Ker(\alpha)$. Thus, by Corollary 2.4.3, $Ker(\alpha)$ is a subgroup of G.

2.7.4 Definition. *Let G and H be groups and let α be a homomorphism from G to H.*

1) *If α is onto H, α is called an* **epimorphism.**

2) *If α is one-to-one, α is called a* **monomorphism.**

3) *If α is both an epimorphism and a monomorphism, then α is called an* **isomorphism.** *If α is an isomorphism, then G and H are said to be* **isomorphic,** *and we write $G \cong H$.*

The concepts of isomorphism and isomorphic groups are extremely important. When we say two groups G and H are isomorphic, we know that there is a one-to-one mapping from one of the groups onto the other and, in addition, that this mapping preserves the binary operations of the groups. Hence G and H are essentially the same group; their elements may be called different names, but the groups have identically the same structure. Furthermore, if one group has certain additional properties, other than those satisfying G1—G4, then quite often, because the groups are isomorphic, the second group will also have the additional properties. For instance, (3) of the following theorem states that the property of being abelian is preserved by isomorphisms.

2.7.5 Theorem. *Let G and H be groups and let α be a homomorphism from G to H. Then*

1) *α is an epimorphism if and only if $Im(\alpha) = H$,*

2) *α is a monomorphism if and only if $Ker(\alpha) = \{e_G\}$ where e_G is the identity element of G, and*

3) *if α is an isomorphism, then G is abelian if and only if H is abelian.*

Proof. We will prove (2) and leave (1) and (3) as exercises. Suppose α is a monomorphism and let e_G, e_H be the identity elements of G and H respectively. By Theorem 2.7.3, $\alpha(e_G) = e_H$. But since α is one-to-one, e_G is the only element of G mapped to the element e_H. Hence $Ker(\alpha) = \{e_G\}$. Conversely, suppose $Ker(\alpha) = \{e_G\}$. Let $g_1, g_2 \in G$ and suppose $\alpha(g_1) = \alpha(g_2)$. Then

$$
\begin{aligned}
e_H &= \alpha(g_1) * \left(\alpha(g_2)\right)^{-1} \\
&= \alpha(g_1) * \alpha(g_2^{-1}) \quad\quad \text{(Theorem 2.7.3)} \\
&= \alpha(g_1 \cdot g_2^{-1}). \quad\quad\;\; \text{(α is a homomorphism)}
\end{aligned}
$$

Therefore $g_1 \cdot g_2^{-1} \in Ker(\alpha) = \{e_G\}$, and so $g_1 \cdot g_2^{-1} = e_G$. Thus

$$
g_1 = g_1 \cdot (g_2^{-1} \cdot g_2) = (g_1 \cdot g_2^{-1}) \cdot g_2 = e_G \cdot g_2 = g_2.
$$

We have shown that $\alpha(g_1) = \alpha(g_2)$ implies $g_1 = g_2$ for all $g_1, g_2 \in G$. Hence α is one-to-one and so α is a monomorphism.

Homomorphisms play an important role in the development of the theory of any algebraic system. In the next chapter on rings, we will again study homomorphisms and their relations to the algebraic system in which they operate.

2.7.6 Exercises

1. Define a mapping β from the group M of 2×2 matrices over I to the group I of all integers (i.e., $\beta: M \to I$) by

$$
\beta\left(\begin{pmatrix} a & b \\ c & d \end{pmatrix}\right) = a \quad\quad \text{for all } \begin{pmatrix} a & b \\ c & d \end{pmatrix} \in M.
$$

The binary operations on M and I are addition. Probe that β is a homomorphism. Is β an epimorphism? A monomorphism?

2. Define a mapping δ from I to the group of even integers by $\delta(n) = 2n$ for all $n \in I$. Prove or disprove that δ is a homomorphism.

3. Let α be a homomorphism from a group G to a group H. Prove the following:
   a) $Im(\alpha)$ is a subgroup of H.
   b) $Ker(\alpha)$ is a normal subgroup of G.
   c) $Im(\alpha) = H$ if and only if α is an epimorphism.

4. Let α be an isomorphism from a group G to a group H. Prove that G is abelian if and only if H is abelian.

5. Prove that every cyclic group of order n is isomorphic to $I/(n)$ for every positive integer n.

6. Let H be a normal subgroup of a group G. Define a mapping $\varphi: G \to G/H$ by

$$\varphi(g) = gH$$

for all $g \in G$. Prove that φ is an epimorphism and that $Ker(\varphi) = H$. This mapping is called the *canonical epimorphism*.

7. Let $\alpha: G \to H$ be a homomorphism. Let $K = Ker(\alpha)$ and $H' = Im(\alpha)$. Prove that $G/K \cong H'$.   (Hint: Define a second mapping $\beta: G/K \to H'$ by $\beta(gK) = \alpha(g)$ for all $g \in G$. Then prove β is well defined and is an isomorphism.) This exercise is known as *The Fundamental Theorem of Homomorphisms*.

8. Let G, H be groups with normal subgroups K, L respectively.   Suppose $G/K \cong H/L$. If $o(G) = 24$ and $o(H) = 18$, what relationship is there between $o(K)$ and $o(L)$?

ADDITIONAL REFERENCES FOR CHAPTER 2

BARNES, WILFRED E., *Introduction to Abstract Algebra*, Boston: Heath and Company (1963).

HERSTEIN, I. N., *Topics in Algebra*, New York: Blaisdell (1964).

McCOY, NEAL H., *Introduction to Modern Algebra*, Boston: Allyn and Bacon (1960).

WHITESITT, J. ELDON, *Principles of Modern Algebra*, Reading, Massachusetts: Addison-Wesley (1964).

CHAPTER 3

RINGS

In this chapter we introduce another algebraic system called a ring. We will define ring and prove several elementary theorems about rings. Then several examples will be considered in detail before we study subrings and ideals and homomorphisms and isomorphisms.

A ring is, first of all, a nonempty set. However, it differs from a group in that a ring must have two binary operations defined on it instead of just one, as in a group. Each of the binary operations must satisfy certain axioms, and both must satisfy an axiom relating the two binary operations. As will be clear later, these axioms are chosen because of the many concrete examples which satisfy them.

3.1 DEFINITION OF A RING

3.1.1 Definition. *A nonempty set R is said to be a **ring** if there are defined on R two binary operations, denoted by $+$ and $\cdot$ and called addition and multiplication, which satisfy the following axioms.*

R1 $a + b \in R$ *for all $a, b \in R$.*   (*closure law of addition*)

R2 $(a + b) + c = a + (b + c)$ *for all $a, b, c \in R$.*
                       (*associative law of addition*)

R3 *There exists an element $0 \in R$ such that $0 + a = a$ for all $a \in R$.*
                       (*existence of additive identity*)

R4 *For each $a \in R$, there exists $x \in R$ such that $a + x = 0$.*
                       (*existence of additive inverses*)

R5 $a + b = b + a$ *for all $a, b \in R$.*
                       (*commutative law of addition*)

R6 $a \cdot b \in R$ *for all $a, b \in R$.*   (*closure law of multiplication*)

R7 $(a \cdot b) \cdot c = a \cdot (b \cdot c)$ *for all $a, b, c \in R$.*
                       (*associative law of multiplication*)

R8 $a \cdot (b + c) = (a \cdot b) + (a \cdot c)$ *and*
$(a + b) \cdot c = (a \cdot c) + (b \cdot c)$ *for all $a, b, c \in R$.*
                       (*distributive laws*)

Notice that axioms R1–R4 simply state that a ring is a group under the binary operation addition; i.e., if one ignores the binary operation called multiplication, the set R and the binary operation called addition fulfill the requirements that R be a group. Furthermore, R5 states that R considered as a group with binary operation addition is abelian. Consequently, axioms R1–R5 may be summarized by saying that R is an abelian group with binary operation addition. Axiom R6 is simply a reiteration of the fact that multiplication is a binary operation on R. Axiom R7 states that multiplication is associative. Axiom R8 shows the relationship between addition and multiplication. In particular, R8 states that multiplication is right-distributive and left-distributive over addition.

In view of the above discussion, we can restate the definition of a ring in the following way.

3.1.2 Definition (alternative). *A nonempty set R is said to be a **ring** if there is defined on R two binary operations $+$ and $\cdot$ such that*

a) *R is an abelian group with respect to $+$,*
b) *$\cdot$ is an associative binary operation on R, and*
c) *$\cdot$ is left- and right-distributive over $+$.*

Let us consider the additive group of R for a moment. We proved in Section 2.2 that the identity element was unique and that each element had a unique inverse. Applying these facts to the additive group of R tells us that the additive identity of R is unique and that each element has a unique additive inverse. We will use the symbol 0 for the unique additive identity of R, and we call 0 the *zero* of the ring R. For each element a of R, its unique inverse will be denoted by $-a$ and will be called "negative a."

The most obvious example of a ring is the set I of integers with the usual addition and multiplication. That the axioms R1–R8 hold for I follows from well-known properties of the addition and multiplication of integers. The zero of the ring is the integer "zero." Another easy example of a ring is the set Q of all rational numbers with the ordinary addition and multiplication.

Compared with the addition on a ring R, the multiplication on R is relatively unknown to us. For instance, the definition of ring does not guarantee the existence of a multiplicative identity; nor does it guarantee the existence of multiplicative inverses. Moreover, the multiplication may not be commutative. Therefore, we consider several special classes of rings.

3.1.3 Definition. *Let R be a ring. We say R is a **ring with unity element** if there exists $e \in R$ such that $a \cdot e = e \cdot a = a$ for all $a \in R$. If such an element e exists, it is called a **unity element** of R.*

3.1.4 Definition. *Let R be a ring with unity element. We say R is a **division ring** if for each nonzero element $a \in R$, there exists an element $x \in R$ such that $a \cdot x = x \cdot a = e$ where e is a unity element of R. If such an x exists, we say x is a **multiplicative inverse of a**.*

In other words, a ring R with unity element is a *division ring* if each nonzero element of R has a *multiplicative inverse* in R. Observe that in order that the multiplicative inverse of a nonzero element a of R may be discussed, R must have a unity element.

3.1.5 Definition. *Let R be a ring. Then R is said to be a* **commutative ring** *if $a \cdot b = b \cdot a$ for all $a, b \in R$.*

If $c \cdot d \neq d \cdot c$ for some pair of elements c, d of a ring R, we say R is a *noncommutative ring*.

The ring I of integers and the ring Q of rational numbers both have a unity element—namely 1. Furthermore, one can easily see that both are commutative. But Q is a division ring, whereas I is not. For any nonzero element a/b of Q, $b/a \in Q$ and $(a/b)(b/a) = (b/a)(a/b) = 1$. On the other hand, $3 \in I$ has no multiplicative inverse in I, so I is not a division ring.

Notice that a commutative ring need not have a unity element and, moreover, a ring with unity element need not be commutative. Examples will be given (Section 3.3) of rings which are commutative and have a unity element, which are noncommutative and have a unity element, which are commutative and do not have a unity element, and which are noncommutative and do not have a unity element. Those examples will establish the complete independence of Definitions 3.1.2 and 3.1.4. It is worthwhile to note also that a division ring need not be commutative.

3.2 SIMPLE PROPERTIES OF A RING

In this section we state and prove some elementary properties of a ring. First of all, we show that, if a ring has a unity element, it is unique. As in Section 2.2, to prove uniqueness of the unity element, we assume that there are two and then prove that they are equal. The details are left as an exercise.

3.2.1 Theorem. *Let R be a ring with unity element. Then the unity element of R is unique.*

Observe that, since a ring need not have a unity element, it was necessary in Theorem 3.2.1 to require that R have a unity element in order to prove that it was unique.

Next we show that if a nonzero element of a ring with unity element has a multiplicative inverse, the multiplicative inverse must be unique. We will follow the same procedure for proving uniqueness that was used before.

3.2.2 Theorem. *Let R be a ring with unity element e and let a be a nonzero element of R which has a multiplicative inverse in R. Then the multiplicative inverse of a is unique.*

Proof. Let s and t be multiplicative inverses of a. Then, by definition of multiplicative inverses,

(1) $$a \cdot s = s \cdot a = e$$

and

(2) $$a \cdot t = t \cdot a = e.$$

Then

$$
\begin{aligned}
s &= s \cdot e && \text{(definition of unity element)} \\
&= s \cdot (a \cdot t) && \text{(by (2))} \\
&= (s \cdot a) \cdot t && \text{(associative law of multiplication)} \\
&= e \cdot t && \text{(by (1))} \\
&= t \cdot && \text{(definition of unity element)}
\end{aligned}
$$

Hence $s = t$, so that the multiplicative inverse of a is unique, as asserted.

Since we now know that if an element a of a ring with unity has a multiplicative inverse, it is unique, then we may speak of "the" multiplicative inverse of a. The symbol a^{-1} will be used to denote the unique multiplicative inverse of the element a.

An effort must be made to avoid confusion because of the terminology associated with the two binary operations addition and multiplication defined on a ring. Since there are two binary operations, a ring may have two identities—one for each binary operation. The additive identity will always be denoted by 0 and called the "zero of the ring" and the multiplicative identity will be denoted by either e or 1 and called the "unity element of the ring." Similarly each nonzero element x of a ring may have two inverses. The additive inverse of x is denoted by $-x$ and is called "negative x" or "the negative of x," whereas the multiplicative inverse of x is denoted by x^{-1} and is called "the multiplicative inverse of x." Furthermore, R5 guarantees that the addition of a ring is always commutative; hence, when one speaks of the commutativity or noncommutativity of a ring, one is referring to the multiplication.

3.2.3 Theorem. *Let 0 be the zero of a ring R. Then*

$$a \cdot 0 = 0 \cdot a = 0$$

for all $a \in R$.

Proof. Let $a \in R$. Then $a = a + 0$. Multiply both sides of this equation on the right by a. Thus

$$a \cdot a = (a + 0) \cdot a = a \cdot a + 0 \cdot a$$

by the right-distributivity of $\cdot$ over $+$. Thus

(1) $$a \cdot a + 0 = a \cdot a + 0 \cdot a.$$

Since R is a group with respect to addition, we can apply Theorem 2.2.2 (Cancellation Law of Addition) to (1). Thus $0 = 0 \cdot a$. That $0 = a \cdot 0$ can be proved in a similar manner.

Theorem 3.2.3 allows us to prove several computational results. For convenience of notation, we will write $a - b$ instead of $a + (-b)$ for elements a, b of a ring.

3.2.4 Theorem. *Let a, b, c be arbitrary elements of a ring R. Then the following are true.*

1) $a \cdot (-b) = -(a \cdot b)$.
2) $(-a) \cdot b = -(a \cdot b)$.
3) $(-a) \cdot (-b) = a \cdot b$.
4) $a \cdot (b - c) = (a \cdot b) - (a \cdot c)$.
5) $(a - b) \cdot c = (a \cdot c) - (b \cdot c)$.

Proof. We will prove (1) and leave the remaining parts as exercises. Note that $-(a \cdot b)$ is the symbol for the unique additive inverse of $a \cdot b$, and observe that

$$
\begin{aligned}
(a \cdot b) + a \cdot (-b) &= a \cdot \big(b + (-b)\big) && \text{(distributive law)} \\
&= a \cdot (0) && \text{(definition of } -b) \\
&= 0. && \text{(Theorem 3.2.3)}
\end{aligned}
$$

Since addition is commutative in R,

$$ a \cdot (-b) + a \cdot b = 0. $$

These two expressions imply that $a \cdot (-b)$ is also an additive inverse of $a \cdot b$. Since the additive inverse of $a \cdot b$ is unique, we must have

$$ a \cdot (-b) = -(a \cdot b). $$

3.2.5 Notation. It is quite common to use *juxtaposition* to indicate multiplication; i.e., one may write ab for $a \cdot b$. Furthermore, multiplication will always take preference over addition, so that $ab + ac$ means $(a \cdot b) + (a \cdot c)$. For convenience, these notational conventions will be used throughout the rest of this book. Their value can be seen by comparing (4) and (5) of Theorem 3.2.4 with the same statements when they are expressed in the following form:

4) $a(b - c) = ab - ac$
5) $(a - b)c = ac - bc$.

However, there will be instances when the original notation using $\cdot$ to indicate multiplication is retained for clarity and emphasis.

3.2.6 Exercises

1. Prove Theorem 3.2.1.
2. Use the fact that $0 + 0 = 0$ to obtain a different proof of Theorem 3.2.3.
3. Suppose R is a ring such that $x^2 = x$ for all $x \in R$. Prove that R is commutative.
4. Prove parts (2) through (5) of Theorem 3.2.4.

3.3 EXAMPLES OF RINGS

In this section several examples of rings will be discussed. For each example, the reader should verify that all the axioms R1–R8 for a ring hold; in particular, the zero and the additive inverse should be made explicit. The reader should also answer the following questions with regard to each example. Does the ring have a unity element? What is it? If the ring has a unity element, which elements have multiplicative inverses? Is the ring commutative?

Example 1. Let E be the set of even integers. Let $+$ and $\cdot$ be the ordinary addition and multiplication of integers respectively. Then E is a commutative ring. However E does not have a unity element since there is no even integer e such that $x \cdot e = x$ for all even integers x.

Example 2. Let I be the set of all integers and let n be a fixed positive integer. We have shown that the definition

$$a \equiv b \ (\text{mod } n) \qquad \text{if } a - b \text{ is a multiple of } n$$

defines an equivalence relation on I. In Example 2 of Section 2.3, we showed that the integers modulo n

$$I/(n) = \{[0], [1], \ldots, [n-1]\}$$

are an abelian group with addition defined by

$$[m] + [k] = [m + k]$$

for all $[m], [k] \in I/(n)$. The reader should review that work.

Define a multiplication of $I/(n)$ by setting

$$[m] \cdot [k] = [mk]$$

for all $[m], [k] \in I/(n)$. To show that $I/(n)$ is a ring with respect to this addition and multiplication, we need only to show that the multiplication is well defined and associative and that the distributive laws hold. The associativity part is included here, and the rest is left as an exercise.

Let $[m]$, $[k]$, and $[j] \in I/(n)$. Then $[m] \cdot ([k] \cdot [j]) = [m] \cdot [kj] = [m(kj)] = [(mk)j] = [mk] \cdot [j] = ([m] \cdot [k]) \cdot [j]$, proving that the multiplication of $I/(n)$ is associative.

Example 3. Let M denote the set of 2×2 matrices over the ring of integers; i.e., M consists of all symbols of the form

$$\begin{pmatrix} a & b \\ c & d \end{pmatrix}$$

where $a, b, c, d \in I$. (See Example 3, Section 2.3.) Recall that two elements

$$\begin{pmatrix} a & b \\ c & d \end{pmatrix} \quad \text{and} \quad \begin{pmatrix} e & f \\ g & h \end{pmatrix}$$

of M are equal if and only if $a = e$, $b = f$, $c = g$, and $d = h$. Addition is defined by the formula

$$\begin{pmatrix} a & b \\ c & d \end{pmatrix} + \begin{pmatrix} e & f \\ g & h \end{pmatrix} = \begin{pmatrix} a + e & b + f \\ c + g & d + h \end{pmatrix}$$

for all

$$\begin{pmatrix} a & b \\ c & d \end{pmatrix}, \begin{pmatrix} e & f \\ g & h \end{pmatrix} \in M.$$

In Example 3 of Section 2.3, we verified that M is an abelian group with this addition. The additive identity (i.e., the zero) is

$$\begin{pmatrix} 0 & 0 \\ 0 & 0 \end{pmatrix}$$

and the additive inverse of an element

$$\begin{pmatrix} a & b \\ c & d \end{pmatrix} \quad \text{of } M \text{ is} \quad \begin{pmatrix} -a & -b \\ -c & -d \end{pmatrix}.$$

Now define a multiplication of matrices by

$$\begin{pmatrix} a & b \\ c & d \end{pmatrix} \cdot \begin{pmatrix} e & f \\ g & h \end{pmatrix} = \begin{pmatrix} ae + bg & af + bh \\ ce + dg & cf + dh \end{pmatrix}$$

for all

$$\begin{pmatrix} a & b \\ c & d \end{pmatrix}, \begin{pmatrix} e & f \\ g & h \end{pmatrix} \in M.$$

Then it is easy to show that this multiplication is associative and that the distributive laws hold. We will show that one distributive law holds and leave to the reader the remainder of the verification that M is a ring with the addition and multiplication defined here. Let

$$\begin{pmatrix} a & b \\ c & d \end{pmatrix}, \begin{pmatrix} e & f \\ g & h \end{pmatrix} \quad \text{and} \quad \begin{pmatrix} m & n \\ p & q \end{pmatrix}$$

be arbitrary elements of M. Then

$$\begin{pmatrix} a & b \\ c & d \end{pmatrix} \cdot \left[\begin{pmatrix} e & f \\ g & h \end{pmatrix} + \begin{pmatrix} m & n \\ p & q \end{pmatrix} \right]$$

$$= \begin{pmatrix} a & b \\ c & d \end{pmatrix} \cdot \begin{pmatrix} e+m & f+n \\ g+p & h+q \end{pmatrix}$$

$$= \begin{pmatrix} a(e+m)+b(g+p) & a(f+n)+b(h+g) \\ c(e+m)+d(g+p) & c(f+n)+d(h+g) \end{pmatrix}$$

$$= \begin{pmatrix} (ae+am)+(bg+bp) & (af+an)+(bh+bq) \\ (ce+cm)+(dg+dp) & (cf+cn)+(dh+dq) \end{pmatrix}$$

$$= \begin{pmatrix} ae+bg & af+bh \\ ce+dg & cf+dh \end{pmatrix} + \begin{pmatrix} am+bp & an+bq \\ cm+dp & cn+dq \end{pmatrix}$$

$$= \begin{pmatrix} a & b \\ c & d \end{pmatrix} \cdot \begin{pmatrix} e & f \\ g & h \end{pmatrix} + \begin{pmatrix} a & b \\ c & d \end{pmatrix} \cdot \begin{pmatrix} m & n \\ p & q \end{pmatrix},$$

proving that multiplication is left-distributive over addition. The ring M has a unity element, namely

$$\begin{pmatrix} 1 & 0 \\ 0 & 1 \end{pmatrix}.$$

However, M is not commutative. (Find a counterexample showing M is not commutative.)

The ring I of integers is a commutative ring with unity element; E of Example 1 is commutative but does not have a unity element; and M of Example 3 has a unity element but is not commutative. Furthermore, the set N of all 2×2 matrices over E, i.e., all symbols of the form

$$\begin{pmatrix} r & s \\ u & v \end{pmatrix}$$

where r, s, u, v are *even* integers, with the addition and multiplication as defined in Example 3, is a ring which is not commutative and does not have a unity element. These four examples establish the independence of the notions of commutativity and the existence of a unity element, as was promised in the discussion following Definition 3.1.5.

Example 4. Let R be the set $\{a, b, c, d\}$, and define addition and multiplication by these tables.

+	a	b	c	d
a	a	b	c	d
b	b	a	d	c
c	c	d	b	a
d	d	c	a	b

·	a	b	c	d
a	a	a	a	a
b	a	a	b	a
c	a	b	c	d
d	a	a	d	a

It is routine to verify that R is an abelian group with respect to addition. We can shorten the work of showing that R is a ring if we observe first that c is the unity element. Thus, since a times any other element is a, to show that R is commutative, we need to show only that $b \cdot d = d \cdot b$. That this is true can readily be seen from the table. Now let us verify that the multiplication is associative. Because of the observations above, it is sufficient to show that $b(bd) = (bb)d$ and $(bd)d = b(dd)$. But the following can also be seen from the table: $b(bd) = ba = a = ad = (bb)d$ and $(bd)d = ad = a = ba = b(dd)$. The verification of the distributive laws is left as an exercise. Note that since R is commutative, we need only verify that multiplication is left-distributive over addition. It is interesting to note that the only element of R which has a multiplicative inverse is c.

Example 5. Let S be a fixed set. Let R be the set of all subsets of S. We define an addition and a multiplication on R by

$$A + B = \{x \in S \mid x \in A \text{ or } x \in B, \text{ but } x \notin A \cap B\}$$

and

$$A \cdot B = A \cap B$$

for all $A, B \in R$ (i.e., for all subsets A, B of S). Then clearly for $A, B \in R$, $A + B$ and $A \cdot B$ are elements of R. Moreover, it is clear that for all $A, B, C \in R$, $A + B = B + A$, $A \cdot B = B \cdot A$, and $(A \cdot B) \cdot C = A \cdot (B \cdot C)$ by definition of $+$ and properties of the intersection of sets. A pictorial description of $A + B$ is given by the Venn diagram in Fig. 3.1, where A is the circle on the left, B is the circle on the right and $A + B$ is the shaded area. The zero is the empty set $\emptyset$ since $A + \emptyset = A$ for all $A \in R$. The additive inverse of an element A of R is the set A itself. The associativity of addition and one of the distributive laws can be verified or can be illustrated using Venn diagrams. Thus R is a ring; this ring is called the *ring of all subsets of S*. Does this ring have a unity element? What is it?

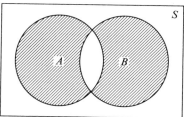

Figure 3.1

Example 6. For this example the student must recall some elementary facts from calculus. The symbol [0, 1] will denote the set $\{x \mid x \text{ is a real number and } 0 \le x \le 1\}$. Recall that if f is a continuous function on [0, 1], then for $x \in [0, 1]$ $f(x)$ is the *value of f at x*. Let C be the set of all continuous functions on [0, 1]. Recall the definition of equality of functions

(Section 2.2). For $f, g \in C$, define their sum $f + g$ by $(f + g)(x) = f(x) + g(x)$ for all $x \in [0, 1]$; i.e., the value of $f + g$ at x is the sum of the value of f at x and the value of g at x. Also for $f, g \in C$, define the product fg of f and g by $(fg)(x) = f(x)g(x)$ for all $x \in [0, 1]$; i.e., the value of fg at x is the product of the values of f and g at x.

From our experience with calculus, we know that the sum of continuous functions on $[0, 1]$ is a continuous function on $[0, 1]$ and the product of continuous functions on $[0, 1]$ is a continuous function on $[0, 1]$. Also if f, g, and h are elements of C, then for all $x \in [0, 1]$,

$$
\begin{aligned}
[(f + g) + h](x) &= (f + g)(x) + h(x) \\
&= (f(x) + g(x)) + h(x) \\
&= f(x) + (g(x) + h(x)) \quad \text{(associativity of the} \\
&= f(x) + (g + h)(x) \quad\quad \text{real numbers)} \\
&= [f + (g + h)](x).
\end{aligned}
$$

Therefore $(f + g) + h = f + (g + h)$. Similarly, one shows that $(fg)h = f(gh)$. Furthermore, the commutativity of addition and multiplication on C is inherited from the real numbers as well as the distributivity of multiplication over addition.

What is the zero? Let $\bar{0}$ be the function on $[0, 1]$ defined by $\bar{0}(x) = 0$ for all $x \in [0, 1]$; i.e., $\bar{0}$ is a constant function. Then for any $f \in C$, $(f + \bar{0})(x) = f(x) + \bar{0}(x) = f(x) + 0 = f(x)$ for all $x \in [0, 1]$. Thus $f + \bar{0} = f$ and so $\bar{0}$ is the zero. For each $f \in C$, we let f^* be the function defined by $f^*(x) = -f(x)$ for all $x \in [0, 1]$. Then $f + f^* = \bar{0}$ since $(f + f^*)(x) = f(x) + f^*(x) = f(x) - f(x) = 0 = \bar{0}(x)$ for all $x \in [0, 1]$. Hence f^* is negative f. This proves that C is a commutative ring! Does C have a unity element?

3.3.1 Exercises

1. Which of the following sets and binary operations are rings? Of those that are rings, which have a unity element? Which are division rings? Which are commutative?

a) $P = \{m + n\sqrt{2} \mid m, n \in I\}$ with the usual addition and multiplication.
b) $M = \{m - n\sqrt{2} \mid m, n \in I\}$ with the usual addition and multiplication.
c) $K =$ set of 2×2 matrices of the form

$$
\begin{pmatrix} a & b \\ 0 & c \end{pmatrix}
$$

where $a, b, c \in I$ with the usual addition and multiplication of matrices.
d) $T = \{(s, t, u) \mid s, t, u \in I\}$ with addition and multiplication defined by

$$(s, t, u) + (x, y, z) = (s + x, t + y, u + z)$$

and

$$(s, t, u) \cdot (x, y, z) = (sx, sy + tz, uz)$$

for all $(s, t, u), (x, y, z) \in T$.

e) $U = \{u, v, w, x\}$ and addition and multiplication are defined by the following tables.

+	u	v	w	x
u	u	v	w	x
v	v	u	x	w
w	w	x	u	v
x	x	w	v	u

·	u	v	w	x
u	u	u	u	u
v	u	u	u	u
w	u	v	w	x
x	u	v	w	x

You may assume that both addition and multiplication are associative in U.

2. Prove that the multiplication in $I/(n)$ is well defined. Verify that the distributive laws hold in $I/(n)$. Also prove that $I/(n)$ is a commutative ring with unity element.

3. Write out addition and multiplication tables for $I/(5)$ and $I/(6)$. Is either a division ring? What can you conjecture about $I/(n)$?

4. Define addition $\oplus$ and multiplication $\odot$ on the set of integers by

$$m \oplus n = m + n - 1$$

and

$$m \odot n = m \oplus n - mn$$

for all $m, n \in I$. Prove that I is a commutative ring with unity element and with these definitions of addition and multiplication.

5. Following are the addition and multiplication tables for a ring having four elements $\{a, b, c, d\}$.

+	a	b	c	d
a	a	b	c	d
b	b	c	d	a
c	c	d	a	b
d	d	a	b	c

·	a	b	c	d
a	a	a	a	a
b	a	–	a	c
c	a	a	a	–
d	a	c	a	–

Use the distributive laws to fill in the blanks in the multiplication table.

6. Let R be a ring with unity element e which has more than one element; prove that $e \neq 0$.

3.4 GENERALIZED SUMS AND PRODUCTS

Let R be a ring and let $a_1, a_2, \ldots, a_n$ be a collection of elements from R. The addition of R is a binary operation, so we know how to add any *two* of these elements. But what if we desire to add three or more of them together? If so, we must define precisely what is meant by the sum of more than two elements. For three elements we define

$$a_1 + a_2 + a_3 = (a_1 + a_2) + a_3.$$

By the associativity of addition, $a_1 + a_2 + a_3 = a_1 + (a_2 + a_3)$; therefore the way we group the terms is irrelevant. In general, we must make an inductive definition.

3.4.1 Definition. *Let R be a ring and let $a_1, a_2, \ldots, a_{k+1}$ be elements of R. Whenever $a_1 + \cdots + a_k$ is defined, define*

$$a_1 + \cdots + a_{k+1} = (a_1 + \cdots + a_k) + a_{k+1}.$$

Thus, by the Principle of Mathematical Induction, the sum of any finite number of elements of a ring is defined. Such a sum is referred to as a *generalized sum*.

3.4.2 Theorem. *Let R be a ring and let n be any positive integer. Then for elements $a_1, \ldots, a_n$ of R,*

$$a_1 + \cdots + a_n = (a_1 + \cdots + a_s) + (a_{s+1} + \cdots + a_n)$$

where s is any integer such that $1 \leq s < n$. In other words, the sum of $a_1, \ldots, a_n$ with parentheses in any position is equal to $a_1 + \cdots + a_n$, as defined above.

Proof. The proof will be by mathematical induction. Let S_n be the statement of the theorem. For $n = 2$, we have $a_1 + a_2 = a_1 + a_2$. Hence S_2 is true. Assume that S_k is true; i.e., assume that

$$a_1 + \cdots + a_k = (a_1 + \cdots + a_s) + (a_{s+1} + \cdots + a_k)$$

where s is any integer such that $1 \leq s < k$. Then for $1 \leq s < k$, we have

$$
\begin{aligned}
a_1 + \cdots + a_{k+1} &= (a_1 + \cdots + a_k) + a_{k+1} && \text{(by 3.4.1)} \\
&= ((a_1 + \cdots + a_s) + (a_{s+1} + \cdots + a_k)) + a_{k+1} && \\
& && \text{(by } S_k\text{)} \\
&= (a_1 + \cdots + a_s) + ((a_{s+1} + \cdots + a_k) + a_{k+1}) && \\
& && \text{(by R2)} \\
&= (a_1 + \cdots + a_s) + (a_{s+1} + \cdots + a_{k+1}). && \\
& && \text{(by 3.4.1)}
\end{aligned}
$$

Furthermore, if $s = k$, then

$$a_1 + \cdots + a_{k+1} = (a_1 + \cdots + a_s) + (a_{s+1} + \cdots + a_{k+1})$$

by definition. Consequently S_{k+1} is true. Therefore, by the Principle of Mathematical Induction, S_n is true for all positive integers n. Thus the theorem is proved.

3.4.3 Remark. *Generalized products* are defined similarly to generalized sums. Moreover, since the proof of Theorem 3.4.2 uses only the associativity of addition, the same proof can be used to prove that the generalized product of $a_1, \ldots, a_n$ is $(a_1 \cdots a_s)(a_{s+1} \cdots a_n)$ where s is any integer such that $1 \leq s < n$.

Other formulas can be generalized in a similar fashion. We will list two such generalizations and prove one, leaving the other as an exercise.

3.4.4 Theorem. *Let R be a ring and let n be any positive integer. For $a_1, \ldots, a_n \in R$,*

$$a_1 + \cdots + a_n = a_{i_1} + \cdots + a_{i_n}$$

where $i_1, i_2, \ldots, i_n$ is any rearrangement of $1, 2, \ldots, n$.

3.4.5 Corollary. *Let R be a commutative ring and let n be any positive integer. For $a_1, \ldots, a_n \in R$,*

$$a_1 a_2 \cdots a_n = a_{i_1} a_{i_2} \cdots a_{i_n}$$

where $i_1, i_2, \ldots, i_n$ is any rearrangement of $1, 2, \ldots, n$.

3.4.6 Theorem. *Let R be a ring and let n be any positive integer. For $a, b_1, \ldots, b_n \in R$,*

$$a(b_1 + b_2 + \cdots + b_n) = ab_1 + ab_2 + \cdots + ab_n.$$

Theorem 3.4.4 and Corollary 3.4.5 are *generalized commutative laws*, and Theorem 3.4.6 is a *generalized distributive law*. We will now prove Theorem 3.4.6.

Proof. Let S_n be the statement of the theorem. Then S_2 is true by the distributive law (R8). Assume that S_k is true; i.e., assume that

$$a(b_1 + \cdots + b_k) = ab_1 + \cdots + ab_k.$$

Then

$$
\begin{aligned}
a(b_1 + \cdots + b_{k+1}) &= a\big((b_2 + \cdots + b_k) + b_{k+1}\big) && \text{(by 3.4.1)} \\
&= a(b_1 + \cdots + b_k) + ab_{k+1} && \text{(by R8)} \\
&= (ab_1 + \cdots + ab_k) + ab_{k+1} && \text{(by } S_k) \\
&= ab_1 + \cdots + ab_{k+1} && \text{(by 3.4.1)}
\end{aligned}
$$

Hence S_{k+1} is true, and so, by the Principle of Mathematical Induction, S_n is true for all positive integers n. This proves the theorem.

3.4.7 Exercises

1. Give an explicit definition of generalized product, and state and prove a theorem similar to Theorem 3.4.2.

2. Prove Theorem 3.4.4 and Corollary 3.4.5.

3. Let R be a ring and let n be any positive integer. For $a_1, \ldots, a_n \in R$, prove that

$$(-a_1)(-a_2)\cdots(-a_n) = \begin{cases} a_1 a_2 \cdots a_n & \text{if } n \text{ is even.} \\ -(a_1 a_2 \cdots a_n) & \text{if } n \text{ is odd.} \end{cases}$$

4. Theorem 3.4.6 gives one generalized distributive law. State and prove another generalized distributive law.

3.5 SUBRINGS AND IDEALS

When we studied groups, we investigated subsets of groups that were groups
in their own right. Such subsets were called subgroups and they played an
important role in the development of the theory of groups. Here we carry
out the same procedure for rings.

3.5.1 Definition. *A nonempty set S is a* **subring** *of a ring R if S is a
subset of R and if S itself is a ring with respect to the addition and multiplication of R.*

The ring E or even integers (Example 1 above) is a subring of the ring I
of all integers. The ring N discussed in Example 3 above is a subring of M
of the same example.

The next theorem simplifies the procedure for showing that a subset of a
ring is actually a subring.

3.5.2 Theorem. *Let R be a ring and let S be a nonempty subset of R.
Then S is a subring of R if and only if*

1) $a + b \in S$ *for all* $a, b \in S$,

2) $-a \in S$ *for all* $a \in S$, *and*

3) $a \cdot b \in S$ *for all* $a, b \in S$.

This theorem says that in order to prove a subset S of a ring R is a subring of R, one needs only to prove that addition and multiplication are
closed on S and that every element of S has an additive inverse in S. The
set S "inherits" the other essential properties of a ring from R. The proof
of this theorem is simple and is left as an exercise. Note that (1) and (2)
simply state that S is a subgroup of R under addition.

A comparison of examples shows that subrings do not necessarily inherit
the property of having a unity element, for the ring E of even integers is a
subring of the ring I of all integers, and I has a unity element, whereas E
does not. On the other hand, every subring of a commutative ring is commutative. To see this, let S be a subring of a commutative ring R and let
a, b be elements of S. Since S is a subset of R, a and b must also belong to R.
Since R is commutative, $ab = ba$. Hence, for all $a, b \in S$, $ab = ba$, so S is
commutative.

Next we will consider a very important type of subring.

3.5.3 Definition. *Let R be a ring. A nonempty subset U of R is an* **ideal**
of R if

1) *U is a subring of R, and if,*

2) *for all* $r \in R$, $u \in U$, *ru and ur belong to U.*

In other words, an ideal U of a ring R is a subring of R with the additional property that U "swallows up" multiplication; i.e., the product of an element of U and an element of R must belong to U. Ideals play a role in the development of ring theory similar to the role played by normal subgroups in group theory. However, an intensive study of ideals is beyond the scope of this course. Hence we will end the discussion of subrings and ideals by considering some examples and proving a theorem which characterizes the ideals of the ring of integers.

Example 1. The ring E of even integers is an ideal of the ring I of all integers. We have previously shown that E is a subring of I, so it is sufficient to show that (2) holds. Let $x \in E$ and $n \in I$. Then $x = 2m$ for some integer m. Hence

$$xn = (2m)n = 2(mn) \quad \text{and} \quad nx = n(2m) = 2(nm),$$

and so xn and nx both belong to E. Thus E is an ideal of I.

Example 2. Let R be a commutative ring. Let a be an element of R and let

$$(a) = \{ar \mid r \in R\}.$$

We will show that (a) is an ideal. Two arbitrary elements of (a) are as and at for $s, t \in R$. Then $as + at = a(s + t)$ by the distributive law. Hence $as + at \in (a)$. Also, the additive inverse of as is $a(-s)$ since

$$as + a(-s) = a(s + (-s)) = a \cdot 0 = 0.$$

Moreover, $a(-s) \in (a)$. Finally,

$$(as)(at) = a(s(at)) \in (a).$$

Hence, by Theorem 3.5.2, (a) is a subring of R. Now let $r \in R$ and $as \in (a)$. Then

$$r(as) = (ra)s = (ar)s = a(rs) \in (a),$$

and

$$(as)r = a(sr) \in (a).$$

Hence (a) is an ideal.

This ideal (a) is important enough to warrant a special name.

3.5.4 Definition. *Let R be a commutative ring and let $a \in R$. The ideal $(a) = \{ar \mid r \in R\}$ is called the **principal ideal generated by a**.*

Principal ideals are often associated with commutative rings which have a unity element, for in that case $a \in (a)$. This may not be true if the ring does not have a unity element. As we will see in Theorem 3.5.5, every ideal in I is a principal ideal. But first, another example.

Example 3. Let R be a ring with unity element. If U is an ideal of R such that $1 \in U$, then $U = R$. For, clearly, $U \subseteq R$. Now let r be an arbitrary element of R. Since U is an ideal and $1 \in U$, $r = r \cdot 1 \in U$. Thus $R \subseteq U$ and hence $R = U$, as claimed.

The next theorem tells us that every ideal of the ring I of all integers with ordinary addition and multiplication is a principal ideal.

3.5.5. Theorem *Every ideal of the ring of integers is principal.*

Proof. Let U be an ideal of I. We must show that $U = (v)$ for some $v \in I$. If U consists of the zero element alone, then $U = (0) = \{0 \cdot r \mid r \in I\}$, and hence U is principal. Thus we now assume that U contains a nonzero integer, say u. If u is negative, then $-u \in U$ and $-u$ is positive. Hence there is a smallest positive integer in U. We know such a "smallest" positive integer v exists since the set of positive integers in U is nonempty.

We want to show that $U = (v)$. Clearly $(v) \subseteq U$. Let $w \in U$. By the division algorithm (Lemma 1.6.1), there exist integers q, r such that $w = qv + r$ and $0 \leq r < v$. But since U is an ideal and $v \in U$, we must have $qv \in U$, and thus $r = w - qv \in U$. If $r \neq 0$, then we have $r \in U$ and $0 < r < v$, contradicting the fact that v is the smallest positive integer in U. Hence r must be zero. This implies that $w = qv$; hence $w \in (v)$. Since w is an arbitrary element of U, this proves that $U \subseteq (v)$. Hence $U = (v)$, proving the theorem.

3.5.6 Exercises

1. Prove Theorem 3.5.2.

2. Let L be the set of all 2×2 matrices of the form

$$\begin{pmatrix} a & 0 \\ b & 0 \end{pmatrix}$$

where $a, b \in I$. Show that L is a subring of the ring M of all 2×2 matrices discussed in Example 3, Section 3.3. Is this subring an ideal?

3. a) Let A and B be subrings of a ring R. Prove that $A \cap B$ is a subring.
   b) If A and B are ideals of R, prove that $A \cap B$ is an ideal.

4. If A and B are ideals of a ring R, define $A + B = \{a + b \mid a \in A, b \in B\}$. Prove that $A + B$ is an ideal.

5. Recall the ring C of continuous functions on $[0, 1]$ of Example 6, Section 3.3. Let $D = \{f \in C \mid f(\tfrac{1}{2}) = 0\}$.
   a) Prove that D is an ideal of C.
   b) Prove that the only ideal of C which contains D is C itself.

6. Let R be a ring and let U be an ideal of R. Let R/U be the set of all (additive) left cosets of U in R; that is,

$$R/U = \{r + U \mid r \in R\}.$$

Define addition and multiplication on R/U as follows:

$$(r + U) + (s + U) = (r + s) + U$$

and

$$(r + U) \cdot (s + U) = rs + U$$

for all $r, s \in R$.

a) Prove in detail that this makes R/U into a ring.
b) Point out where you make use of the fact that U is an ideal of R.
c) What properties could R have that will always remain as properties of R/U? For instance, will R commutative imply R/U commutative?

3.6 HOMOMORPHISMS

In Section 2.7, we defined and discussed homomorphisms between two groups. Homomorphisms were defined as those mappings between two groups that preserved the binary operations on those groups. Since rings have two binary operations defined on them, rather than one, it is not unusual that a homomorphism between two rings must preserve both the addition and multiplication of the rings.

3.6.1 Definition. *Let R and S be rings. A (ring)* **homomorphism** *is a mapping α from R to S such that*

(1) $$\alpha(a + b) = \alpha(a) + \alpha(b)$$

and

(2) $$\alpha(a \cdot b) = \alpha(a) \cdot \alpha(b)$$

for all $a, b \in R$.

The name "homomorphism" is used for mappings between groups *and* between rings. No confusion should arise, however; one simply understands that Definition 3.6.1 applies when one is speaking of rings and Definition 2.7.1 applies when one is speaking of groups. To emphasize the fact that the algebraic objects in question are groups or rings, one may use the names "group homomorphism" or "ring homomorphism" for "homomorphism." In (1) above, the addition on the right-hand side is that of the ring S, whereas the addition on the left-hand side is that of the ring R. Similarly, $a \cdot b$ in (2) means multiplication in R and $\alpha(a) \cdot \alpha(b)$ means multiplication in S.

Observe that (1) simply states that α is a group homomorphism from the additive group of R into the additive group of S. Hence the results of Section 2.7 apply. In particular, the following theorem is simply a restatement of Theorem 2.7.3.

3.6.2 Theorem. *Let R and S be rings and let α be a homomorphism from R to S. Then*

1) $\alpha(0) = 0$ *and*

2) *for all* $r \in R$, $\alpha(-r) = -\alpha(r)$.

3.6.3 Definition. *Let R and S be rings and let α be a homomorphism from R to S.*

1) $Im(\alpha) = \{s \in S \mid \alpha(r) = s \text{ for some } r \in R\}$ *is called the* **image set** *under* α.

2) $Ker(\alpha) = \{r \in R \mid \alpha(r) = 0\}$ *is called the* **kernel** *of* α.

3) *If* α *is onto S, then* α *is called an* **epimorphism.**

4) *If* α *is one-to-one, then* α *is called a* **monomorphism.**

5) *If* α *is both an epimorphism and a monomorphism, then* α *is called an* **isomorphism.**

It is important to notice that the kernel of a ring homomorphism is the set of elements whose image is zero, the additive identity of the ring. Consequently, the kernel of a ring homomorphism is just the kernel of the group homomorphism between the additive groups of the rings. Therefore, by Theorem 2.7.3, the kernel of a ring homomorphism is an abelian subgroup of the additive group of the ring on which the homomorphism is defined. In fact, the following theorem is evident from the definitions given above and the results obtained in Section 2.7.

3.6.4 Theorem. *Let α be a homomorphism from the ring R to the ring S Then the following are true.*

1) $Im(\alpha)$ *is a subring of S.*

2) $Ker(\alpha)$ *is a subring of R.*

3) α *is an epimorphism if and only if* $Im(\alpha) = S$.

4) α *is a monomorphism if and only if* $Ker(\alpha) = \{0\}$.

The only assertion of this theorem which has not been proved previously is that $Im(\alpha)$ and $Ker(\alpha)$ are closed with respect to the multiplications in S and R respectively. The proof of this is left as an exercise.

3.6.5 Theorem. *Let α be an isomorphism from a ring R onto a ring S.*

1) *The ring R has a unity element if and only if S has a unity element.*

2) *Suppose R has a unity element. Then R is a division ring if and only if S is a division ring.*

3) *The ring R is commutative if and only if S is commutative.*

Proof. We will prove (1) and leave the proof of (2) and (3) as exercises. Suppose R has a unity element e. Let $s \in S$; since α is an epimorphism, there exists $r \in R$ such that $a(r) = s$. Then $r \cdot e = e \cdot r = r$ and hence, since α is a homomorphism,

$$s = \alpha(r) = \alpha(r \cdot e) = \alpha(r) \cdot \alpha(e) = s \cdot \alpha(e)$$

and

$$s = \alpha(r) = \alpha(e \cdot r) = \alpha(e) \cdot \alpha(r) = \alpha(e) \cdot s.$$

Since s is an arbitrary element of S, this proves that $\alpha(e)$ is the unity element of S.

Conversely, suppose that S has a unity element e'. Since α is an isomorphism, there exists a unique $e \in R$ such that $\alpha(e) = e'$. Let $r \in R$. Then, since α is a homomorphism,

$$\alpha(r \cdot e) = \alpha(r) \cdot \alpha(e) = \alpha(r) \cdot e' = \alpha(r).$$

Since α is one-to-one, this implies that $r \cdot e = r$. Moreover, $\alpha(e \cdot r) = \alpha(r)$ and so $e \cdot r = r$. Hence e is the unity element of R.

The concept of isomorphism between two rings is important enough to deserve additional comment. If R and S are isomorphic rings, then there is a one-to-one mapping from R onto S, and furthermore, this mapping preserves the additive and multiplicative structure. In addition, Theorem 3.6.5 shows that R and S have essentially the same properties. In other words, R and S are essentially the same rings; the only difference is in the naming of the elements of each. Moreover, quite often in modern algebra, one *identifies* the elements of R and the elements of S; i.e., no distinction is made between elements of R and elements of S since they differ only in name.

3.6.6 Exercises

Let R and S denote arbitrary rings.

1. Prove that the mapping $\alpha: R \rightarrow S$ defined by $\alpha(r) = 0$ for all $r \in R$ is a homomorphism. What is $Ker(\alpha)$ and $Im(\alpha)$?

2. Let
   $$P = \{m + n\sqrt{2} \mid m, n \in I\} \quad \text{and} \quad M = \{m - n\sqrt{2} \mid m, n \in I\}.$$

   We have seen that P and M are rings with the usual multiplication and addition. Define a mapping $\alpha: P \rightarrow M$ by $\alpha(m + n\sqrt{2}) = m - n\sqrt{2}$ for all $m + n\sqrt{2} \in P$. Prove or disprove that α is a monomorphism.

3. Recall the rings K and T of Exercise 1(c) and (d), Section 3.3.1. Define a mapping $\beta: K \rightarrow T$ by
   $$\beta\left(\begin{pmatrix} a & b \\ 0 & c \end{pmatrix}\right) = (a, b, c).$$

   Prove that β is an isomorphism.

4. If α is a homomorphism from R to S, prove that
   a) $Ker(\alpha)$ is an ideal of R, and   b) $Im(\alpha)$ is a subring of S.

5. Let α be an isomorphism from R onto S. Let e and e' denote the unity elements of R and S respectively. If an element $r \in R$ has a multiplicative inverse r^{-1}, prove that $\alpha(r^{-1}) = (\alpha(r))^{-1}$. Using this fact, prove Theorem 3.6.5 (2).

6. Prove Theorem 3.6.5 (3).

7. If α is an epimorphism from R onto S, and if U is an ideal of R, then $\alpha(U) = \{\alpha(u) \mid u \in U\}$ is an ideal of S.

ADDITIONAL REFERENCES FOR CHAPTER 3

BARNES, WILFRED E., *Introduction to Abstract Algebra*, Boston: Heath and Company (1963).

HERSTEIN, I. N., *Topics in Algebra*, New York: Blaisdell (1964).

McCOY, NEAL H., *Introduction to Modern Algebra*, Boston: Allyn and Bacon (1960).

WHITESITT, J. ELDON, *Principles of Modern Algebra*, Reading, Massachusetts: Addison-Wesley (1964).

CHAPTER 4

THE INTEGERS

Throughout the preceding discussion it has been assumed that the reader has a general familiarity with the ring of integers and certain properties which it possesses. This chapter presents a closer look at the integers and establishes some rudimentary properties concerning divisibility, primes, the division algorithm, the greatest common divisor and the Euclidean algorithm, and the Fundamental Theorem of Arithmetic.

4.1 DIVISIBILITY AND PRIMES

4.1.1 Definition. *Let* a, $b \in I$. *Then we say* ***a divides b*** *if there exists* $c \in I$ *such that* $b = ac$. *In this case we also say that* a *is a* ***divisor*** *of* b, a *is a* ***factor*** *of* b, *and* b *is a* ***multiple*** *of* a. *If* a *divides* b, *we denote this fact by* $a \mid b$.

The symbol $\nmid$ is used to denote "does not divide"; for example, $3 \nmid 4$. Note that for any integer b, ± 1 and $\pm b$ divide b. Moreover b divides 0 since $0 = b \cdot 0$. Also, if a and b are positive integers and $a \mid b$, then $a \leq b$. To see this, observe that since $a \mid b$, there exists $c \in I$ such that $b = ac$. Since a and b are positive, c must be positive. Hence $c \geq 1$, and if we multiply by a, we get $b = ac \geq a$.

The symbol $\mid$ defines a relation on I. We have seen above that $\mid$ is reflexive. But $\mid$ is not symmetric since $2 \mid 4$, but $4 \nmid 2$. Thus $\mid$ is not an equivalence relation on I. However $\mid$ is transitive; for, suppose $a \mid b$ and $b \mid c$. Then there exist $d, f \in I$ such that $b = da$ and $c = fb$. Then $c = f(da) = (fd)a$ so that $a \mid c$.

Certain integers stand out because of their divisibility properties. These integers are called *primes*.

4.1.2 Definition. *A positive integer* p *is a* ***prime*** *if* $p \neq 1$ *and if the only divisors of* p *are* ± 1 *and* $\pm p$.

Thus, by the definition, if p is a prime, then $p \geq 2$. Some authors do not require that p be positive in order to be a prime. However, in order that "uniqueness" results may be obtained in the discussion of factorization in Section 3, this restriction is necessary. Requiring primes to be positive is not a serious restriction, since "negative primes" can be expressed as -1

times a prime. It is worthwhile to consider the negation of Definition 4.1.2. Suppose $n \in I$ and n is not a prime. Then n is negative, or $n = 0$, or $n = 1$; or if none of these is true, then there exist integers n_1, n_2 such that

$$n = n_1 n_2, \quad \text{and} \quad 1 < n_1 < n, \quad \text{and} \quad 1 < n_2 < n.$$

Primes play an important role in the theory of numbers. In fact, they are the building blocks from which the integers arise. We will prove in Section 3 that every nonzero integer can be expressed uniquely as ± 1 times a product of a finite number of primes. Much of the elementary theory of numbers is devoted to a study of primes—their properties and existence. There are many unsolved problems in number theory dealing with primes. For more information on primes, the reader is referred to contemporary texts in elementary number theory (see references at end of chapter).

Now we repeat a theorem which was included in Section 1.6 in order to make this Chapter complete within itself. Let a, b be positive integers. We want to develop a process by which we can "divide" a by b. We must be careful here since there is no binary operation "division" defined on I. Intuitively, if we consider the number line and mark off multiples of b, then a must either coincide with one of the multiples of b or fall immediately to the right of one of them (Fig. 4.1). Suppose a coincides with or falls immediately to the right of qb. If we denote the line segment from qb to a by r, then we can write $a = qb + r$. Moreover, if a is to the left of $(q + 1)b$, then $0 \leq r < b$. Hence we have "divided" b into a with "quotient" q and "remainder" r. For example, if we divide 67 by 14, we get $67 = 4(14) + 11$.

Figure 4.1

Now let us make this concept precise. The process we have described is called the *Division Algorithm*. The proof uses the fact that the set of non-negative integers is well ordered; that is, given any nonempty subset S of nonnegative integers, S must contain a smallest element.

4.1.3 Theorem (Division Algorithm). *Given any two positive integers a and b, there exist unique integers q, r such that*

(1) $a = bq + r$ and $0 \leq r < b$.

Proof. First we must prove the existence of integers q and r satisfying (1) and then prove that they are unique. Let

$$S = \{a - bx \mid x \in I, a - bx \geq 0\}.$$

Recall that a, b are fixed; so S consists of all nonnegative expressions of the form $a - bx$ as x varies in I. For $x = 0$, $a - bx = a > 0$. Hence $a \in S$, so S is nonempty. Thus, by the well-ordering property of the nonnegative integers, S contains a smallest element, say r. Then $r \in S$, so that there exists $q \in I$ such that $a - bq = r$. Thus $a = bq + r$ and $0 \le r$. To verify that q and r satisfy (1), we must now show that $r < b$. Suppose not; i.e., suppose $r \ge b$. Then $r - b \ge 0$ and

$$r - b = (a - bq) - b = a - (q + 1)b.$$

This proves that $r - b \in S$. But since b is positive, $r > r - b$. This contradicts the fact that r is the smallest element of S. Hence we must have $r < b$. This completes the proof of the existence of q and r.

Now suppose there also exist integers q_1, r_1 such that $a = bq_1 + r_1$ and $0 \le r_1 < b$. Then $bq_1 + r_1 = bq + r$, and hence $b(q_1 - q) = r - r_1$. Without loss of generality, we may assume that $q_1 \ge q$. (For, given that $q_1 \le q$, consider $b(q - q_1) = r_1 - r$, and use the argument given here.) Then $q_1 - q \ge 0$. If $q_1 - q \ne 0$, then $q_1 - q \ge 1$, so that

$$r_1 - r = b(q - q_1) \ge b,$$

contradicting the fact that $b > r_1$ and $b > r$. Hence $q_1 - q = 0$, and consequently $r - r_1 = 0$. Therefore $q_1 = q$ and $r_1 = r$, establishing the uniqueness.

4.1.4 Remark. The hypothesis that b is a positive number can be relaxed to require that b be nonzero by noting that if b is negative, then $-b$ is positive. Hence $a = (-b)(-q) + r$. Furthermore, the restriction that a is positive can also be removed.

Given a and b, if q and r are the unique integers satisfying (1) in Theorem 4.1.3, we call r the *remainder* of dividing a by b, and we call q the *quotient*.

4.1.5 Exercises

Let a, b, c, d, p, q be arbitrary integers.

1. For each pair of numbers given below, find the q and r which satisfy (1) of Theorem 4.1.3.

   a) $a = 162$, $b = 49$ b) $a = 213$, $b = 114$ c) $a = 1032$, $b = -25$

2. Given that $a \mid b$ and $a \mid c$, prove that $a \mid (b \pm c)$.

3. Given that $a \mid b$, prove that $a \mid bc$ for all $c \in I$.

4. Prove or disprove: If $a \mid bc$, then $a \mid b$ or $a \mid c$.

5. Given that $a \mid b$ and $b \mid a$, show that $a = \pm b$. In this case, a and b are said to be *associates*.

6. Suppose $a \mid b$. Prove or disprove the following statements.

   a) $ac \mid bc$ for all $c \in I$.

   b) $a + c \mid b + c$ for all $c \in I$.

   c) If in addition $d \mid b$, then $a + d \mid b$.

7. Let p, q be primes. Given that $p \mid q$, prove that $p = q$.

8. Given that p, q are primes, show that $p \nmid (pq + 1)$ and $q \nmid (pq + 1)$.

9. Given that n is any positive integer and that $p_1, p_2, \ldots, p_n$ are distinct primes, show that $p_1 p_2 \cdots p_n + 1$ is not divisible by any of the primes $p_1, p_2, \ldots, p_n$.

10. Use Exercise 9 to prove that there are infinitely many primes.

11. Given that $a = b + c$ and that d divides any two of the three integers a, b, and c, prove that d must also divide the third.

12. A *prime triple* is a set of three primes of the form n, $n + 2$, $n + 4$ for some positive integers n. Show that 3, 5, 7 is the only prime triple.

13. Show that, given any positive integer n, one can find a sequence of consecutive nonprime positive integers of length n.

4.2 GREATEST COMMON DIVISOR

4.2.1 Definition. *Let a, b be given nonzero integers. The positive integer d is called the **greatest common divisor of a and b** if the following conditions hold.*

1) *$d \mid a$ and $d \mid b$.*

2) *If $e \mid a$ and $e \mid b$ for any $e \in I$, then $e \mid d$.*

Condition (1) states that d must be a common divisor of a and b, and condition (2) implies that d is the "greatest" common divisor. We require that the greatest common divisor of two nonzero integers be positive to obtain uniqueness. Note that if d is the greatest common divisor of a and b, then $-d$ satisfies conditions (1) and (2) also. So far we have no evidence that, given two nonzero integers, we can find their greatest common divisor. We will prove that the greatest common divisor of any two nonzero integers exists, and, in fact, we will show that the greatest common divisor can be expressed in a special form. Then we will develop an algorithm by which we can determine the greatest common divisor of any two nonzero integers.

4.2.2 Theorem. *Let a, b be given nonzero integers. Then the greatest common divisor d of a and b exists; and, in fact, there exist integers m, n such that $d = am + bn$.*

Proof. Let $S = \{ax + by \mid x, y \in I, ax + by > 0\}$. Then, letting $x = a$ and $y = b$, we obtain $a^2 + b^2 \in S$ since $a^2 + b^2 > 0$. Hence S is not empty. Thus, by the well-ordering of the positive integers, S has a least element. Let d be this least element; then $d = am + bn$ for some $m, n \in I$. We will prove that d is the greatest common divisor of a and b.

First we prove that $d \mid a$. That $d \mid b$ is proved similarly. By the division algorithm, there exist integers q, r such that

$$a = qd + r \qquad \text{and} \qquad 0 \le r < d.$$

Then $a = q(am + bn) + r$, so that $r = a(1 - qm) + b(qn)$. Thus, if $r \ne 0$, then $r \in S$. But since $r < d$, this contradicts our choice of d. Hence $r = 0$. Thus $a = qd$, proving that $d \mid a$.

Now suppose $e \mid a$ and $e \mid b$ for some $e \in I$. Then there exist $u, v \in I$ such that $a = eu$ and $b = ev$. Then

$$d = (eu)m + (ev)n = e(um + vn).$$

Therefore $e \mid d$. This proves that d is the greatest common divisor of a and b.

4.2.3 Definition. *Let a, b be given integers. Then an expression of the form $ax + by$ where x and y are integers is called a **linear combination** of a and b.*

This definition allows us to restate Theorem 4.2.2 as the following corollary.

4.2.4 Corollary. *Let a, b be given nonzero integers. Then the greatest common divisor of a, b is the least positive linear combination of a and b.*

4.2.5 Definition. *Two nonzero integers are said to be **relatively prime** if their greatest common divisor is 1.*

Thus two nonzero integers are relatively prime if they have no common factors other than 1. If p is a prime and a is a nonzero integer, than a and p are relatively prime unless a is a multiple of p. Thus two primes are either relatively prime or equal. On the other hand, two nonzero integers can be relatively prime although neither is prime; for instance, 8 and 9 are relatively prime, but neither is prime.

Do not misinterpret Corollary 4.2.4. If a and b are nonzero integers such that $d = ax + by$ for some d, x, $y \in I$, then Corollary 4.2.4 does not imply that d is the greatest common divisor of a and b. Indeed, d is the greatest common divisor of a and b only if d is the *least positive* linear combination of a and b. On the other hand, if a and b are nonzero integers such that $1 = ax + by$ for some $x, y \in I$, then a and b are relatively prime. The greatest common divisor of a and b is 1 since 1 is clearly the least positive linear combination of a and b. Note that $1 = ax + by$ means that x and y, as well as a and y, are also relatively prime.

For convenience, the symbol (a, b) is usually used to denote the greatest common divisor of a and b. This symbol is not to be confused with the ordered pair (a, b). Thus a and b are relatively prime if $(a, b) = 1$. When confusion may arise from the use of this symbol, "greatest common divisor," shortened to g.c.d., is often used.

Theorem 4.2.2 established the existence of the g.c.d. of any two nonzero integers but did not provide a method for finding the g.c.d. of two given nonzero integers. We will now discuss a procedure by which the g.c.d. of any two specific nonzero integers can be computed. This method is known as the *Euclidean Algorithm*.

Let a and b be given nonzero integers. Since $(a, b) = (-a, b)$, we may assume a is positive without loss of generality. By the Division Algorithm (4.1.3 and Remark 4.1.4), there exist integers q_1, r_1 such that

$$a = bq_1 + r_1 \quad \text{and} \quad 0 \le r_1 < b.$$

If $r_1 \ne 0$, divide b by r_1. Then there exist integers q_2, r_2 such that

$$b = r_1 q_2 + r_2 \quad \text{and} \quad 0 \le r_2 < r_1.$$

Continue this process so long as the remainder is nonzero. At each step, the divisor of the previous step is divided by the remainder of the current step, thus producing a new remainder and divisor. After a finite number of steps, we will have the following:

$$
\begin{array}{llll}
(1) & a = bq_1 + r_1 & \text{and} & 0 < r_1 < b, \\
(2) & b = r_1 q_2 + r_2 & \text{and} & 0 < r_2 < r_1, \\
(3) & r_1 = r_2 q_3 + r_3 & \text{and} & 0 < r_3 < r_2, \\
\vdots & \quad\vdots & & \quad\vdots \\
(k-1) & r_{k-3} = r_{k-2} q_{k-1} + r_{k-1} & \text{and} & 0 < r_{k-1} < r_{k-2}, \\
(k) & r_{k-2} = r_{k-1} q_k + r_k & \text{and} & 0 < r_k < r_{k-1}, \\
(k+1) & r_{k-1} = r_k q_{k+1} + 0. & &
\end{array}
$$

We must eventually obtain a 0 remainder since $r_1, r_2, \ldots, r_k$ are positive integers such that

$$r_1 > r_2 > r_3 > \cdots > r_{k-1} > r_k.$$

4.2.6 Theorem (Euclidean Algorithm). *The last nonzero remainder in the process above is the g.c.d. of a and b.*

Proof. We must show that $r_k = (a, b)$. First we show that r_k divides a and b. From $(k + 1)$ it is clear that $r_k \mid r_{k-1}$. Thus, from (k) it follows (Exercise 2, Section 4.1.5) that $r_k \mid r_{k-2}$ (since $r_k \mid r_{k-1} q_k$ and r_k divides itself). Then from $(k - 1)$, a similar argument shows that $r_k \mid r_{k-3}$. Continue! Finally we see that $r_k \mid r_1$ and $r_k \mid r_2$. Thus $r_k \mid b$ by (2). Then from (1) we find that $r_k \mid a$.

Now suppose $e \mid a$ and $e \mid b$. Then from (1), using 4.1.5, Exercise 2, we see that $e \mid r_1$. Similarly from (2), $e \mid r_2$, and so on. Finally, by continuing through each step, we arrive at the conclusion $e \mid r_k$. This proves that r_k is the g.c.d. of a and b.

Let us illustrate by considering a numerical example. Find $(422,68)$.

$$422 = 68 \cdot 6 + 14$$
$$68 = 14 \cdot 4 + 12$$
$$14 = 12 \cdot 1 + 2$$
$$12 = 2 \cdot 6 + 0$$

Thus $(422,68) = 2$.

Theorem 4.2.2 guaranteed that the g.c.d of two nonzero integers a and b is expressible as a linear combination of a and b. The computation of the g.c.d. via the Euclidean Algorithm provides the equations necessary to find the correct linear combination. From (1) we see that

$$r_1 = a - bq_1.$$

Then, combining this with (2), we get

$$r_2 = b - r_1 q_2$$
$$= b - (a - bq_1)q_2$$
$$= -q_2 a + (1 + q_1 q_2)b.$$

Next,

$$r_3 = r_1 - r_2 q_3$$
$$= (a - bq_1) - [(-q_2)a + (1 - q_1 q_2)b]q_3$$
$$= (1 + q_2 q_3)a + (q_1 q_2 q_3 - q_1 - q_3)b.$$

Continue this process until r_k is expressed as a linear combination of a and b.

For the numerical example above where $2 = (422,68)$ we have, letting $a = 422$ and $b = 68$,

$$14 = a - b6,$$
$$12 = b - (a - b6)4 = 25b - 4a,$$
$$2 = 14 - 12 = (a - b6) - (25b - 4a) = 5a - 31b.$$

Thus $2 = (422,68) = 5(422) - 31(68)$.

Now that we have established the existence of the g.c.d. of two nonzero integers, we can prove a theorem which states a very important property of primes.

4.2.7 Theorem. *If a prime p divides a product ab, then p divides a or p divides b.*

Proof. Suppose that $p \mid ab$ and that $p \nmid a$. Since p is a prime, p and a are relatively prime (or else $a = 1$ and the theorem is proved, since $p \mid ab$). Hence there exist integers r, s such that $1 = pr + as$. Now multiply by b; then

$$b = prb + abs.$$

We have p divides prb and p divides abs by hypothesis. Thus, by 4.1.5, Exercise 2, p divides $prb + abs$. Therefore $p \mid b$.

A simple mathematical induction proves the following corollary.

4.2.8 Corollary. *If n is any positive integer, and if a prime p divides a product $a_1 a_2 \cdots a_n$ of integers, then p must divide at least one a_i $(1 \leq i \leq n)$.*

In Definition 4.1.1, we defined "multiple of" as follows: Given two integers a and b, b *is a multiple of* a if there exists an integer c such that $b = ac$. This notion is extended in the following definition.

4.2.9 Definition. *Let a, b be given nonzero integers. The positive integer m is the **least common multiple of a and b** if the following conditions hold.*

1) *The integer m is a multiple of both a and b.*

2) *If n is a multiple of both a and b, then n is a multiple of m.*

Compare this to Definition 4.2.1. We use l.c.m. to abbreviate "least common multiple," and when no confusion can arise, the symbol $[a, b]$ is used to denote the least common multiple of two nonzero integers a, b.

4.2.10 Theorem. *Let a, b be given positive integers. Then the least common multiple of a and b exists; and, in fact,*

(1) $$[a, b](a, b) = ab$$

where (a, b) denotes the greatest common divisor of a and b.

Proof. We will prove that (1) holds. Since we already know that (a, b) exists, that fact will prove that $[a, b]$ exists. Let $d = (a, b)$; i.e., d is the greatest common divisor of a and b. Then there exist $a_0, b_0 \in I$ such that $a = da_0$ and $b = db_0$. Then, by 4.2.11, Exercise 2, $(a_0, b_0) = 1$.

Let f be any common multiple of a and b. Then there exist $r, s \in I$ such that

$$f = ra = ra_0 d \quad \text{and} \quad f = sb = sb_0 d.$$

Thus $b_0 d \mid ra_0 d$, and hence $b_0 \mid ra_0$. But since $(a_0, b_0) = 1$, the result proved in 4.2.11, Exercise 6, implies that $b_0 \mid r$, say $r = b_0 k$. Then $f = ka_0 b_0 d$. Now clearly $a_0 b_0 d$ is a common multiple of a and b and $a_0 b_0 d \mid f$. Hence the least common multiple of a and b is $a_0 b_0 d$. But since $d = (a, b)$, (1) holds as asserted.

Notice that this theorem holds if a and b are simply nonzero integers. In this case

$$[a, b](a, b) = \pm ab$$

since, if either a or b is negative, but not both, then ab is negative, whereas $[a, b]$ and (a, b) are positive.

4.2.11 Exercises

1. Find the g.c.d. and l.c.m. of each of the pairs of integers below. Express the g.c.d. as a linear combination of the integers.

   a) 103 and 62
   b) 1024 and 361
   c) 201 and -1014
   d) 478 and 212

2. Let a and b be nonzero integers and $d = (a, b)$ and $a = a_0 d$ and $b = b_0 d$; prove that $(a_0, b_0) = 1$.

3. Let x, y, z, t be nonzero integers such that $x = yz + t$; show that $(x, z) = (z, t)$.

4. If a, b are nonzero integers and g is a positive integer, then $(ga, gb) = g(a, b)$. Prove it.

5. Prove Corollary 4.2.8.

6. If a, b are nonzero integers such that $(a, b) = 1$ and $a \mid bc$, then $a \mid c$. Prove it.

7. If a, b are nonzero integers such that $d = (a, b)$, then d is precisely the number of integers in the set $\{a, 2a, 3a, \ldots, ba\}$ which are divisible by b. Prove it!

8. Prove that the least common multiple of two positive relatively prime integers is their product.

9. Let a, b, c be nonzero integers. Define the g.c.d. of $a, b,$ and c, and prove it is equal to $((a, b), c) = (a, (b, c))$.

4.3 THE FUNDAMENTAL THEOREM OF ARITHMETIC

Throughout the beginning courses in algebra and arithmetic, one assumption is made without being stated explicitly. This assumption is that each non-zero integer can be "factored" in exactly one way. In this section we will prove that this assumption is valid; in fact, when it is formalized and proved, it is known as *The Fundamental Theorem of Arithmetic*. The proof will be in two parts.

4.3.1 Theorem. *Every integer $a > 1$ can be expressed as a product of finitely many primes.*

Proof. Here "product" must be interpreted correctly. One prime by itself is to be considered a product. Hence all primes are products of primes. Also 1 is the product of zero primes.

Let S be the set of integers greater than one which *cannot* be expressed as a product of finitely many primes. The theorem will be proved by showing that S is empty. Assume S is not empty. Then S is a nonempty set of positive integers and hence must have a smallest element; call it b. Since $b \in S$, b cannot be a prime. Hence there exist integers c, d such that

$$b = cd \quad \text{and} \quad 1 < c < b, \ 1 < d < b.$$

Therefore, since b is the smallest element of S and $1 < c < b$ and $1 < d < b$, then c and d must not be elements of S. That is, c and d can be expressed as a product of finitely many primes; say $c = p_1p_2 \cdots p_n$ and $d = q_1q_2 \cdots q_m$ where $p_1, p_2, \ldots, p_n, q_1, q_2, \ldots, q_m$ are all primes. Then

$$b = cd = p_1p_2 \cdots p_nq_1q_2 \cdots q_m,$$

contradicting the fact that $b \in S$. Hence S is empty and the theorem is proved.

If $a > 1$ can be expressed as $a = p_1p_2p_3 \cdots p_n$ where $p_1, p_2, p_3, \ldots, p_n$ are primes, then also $a = p_2p_1p_3 \cdots p_n$ and $a = p_np_1p_2 \cdots p_{n-1}p_3$, etc. But these expressions for a as a product of primes are not essentially different since exactly the same primes are used in each expression. Consequently, this qualification must be considered in expressing the uniqueness part of the Fundamental Theorem of Arithmetic.

4.3.2 Theorem. *Every integer $a > 1$ can be expressed in only one way as a product of primes except for the order of the factors.*

Proof. As usual, we assume that there are two expressions of a as a product of primes: $a = p_1p_2 \cdots p_n$ and $a = q_1q_2 \cdots q_m$ where $p_1, p_2, \ldots, p_n$, $q_1, q_2, \ldots, q_m$ are primes. We must show that $n = m$ and that the two sets $\{p_1, p_2, \ldots, p_n\}$ and $\{q_1, q_2, \ldots, q_m\}$ are the same. Since $p_1p_2 \cdots p_n = q_1q_2 \cdots q_m$, then $p_1 \mid q_1q_2 \cdots q_m$. By Corollary 4.2.8, p_1 divides q_i for some i $(1 \le i \le m)$. Hence, by 4.1.5, Exercise 7, $p_1 = q_i$. Relabel the q's so that $p_1 = q_1$. Then, using the cancellation law of multiplication, we have that

$$p_2p_3 \cdots p_n = q_2q_3 \cdots q_m.$$

Thus $p_2 \mid q_2q_3 \cdots q_m$, and so $p_2 = q_j$ for some j $(2 \le j \le m)$. Relabel again so that $p_2 = q_2$. By continuing this process, one sees that each p_i is equal to a q_i. Hence

$$\{p_1, p_2, \ldots, p_n\} \subseteq \{q_1, q_2, \ldots, q_m\}.$$

On the other hand, by reversing the roles of the p's and q's in the above argument, one sees that

$$\{q_1, q_2, \ldots, q_m\} \subseteq \{p_1, p_2, \ldots, p_n\}.$$

Hence these two sets are equal. Therefore $n = m$ and, possibly after a relabeling, $p_i = q_i$ for $i = 1, 2, \ldots, n$.

We now combine these results to obtain the following theorem.

4.3.3 The Fundamental Theorem of Arithmetic. *Every nonzero integer a can be expressed uniquely (except for order of the factors) in the form*

$$a = (\pm 1)p_1p_2 \cdots p_n$$

where $p_1, p_2, \ldots, p_n$ are primes.

If $a > 1$, we have already proved the assertion. If $-a > 1$, then by the above, $-a = p_1 p_2 \cdots p_n$ for some primes $p_1, p_2, \ldots, p_n$. Hence $a = (-1)p_1 p_2 \cdots p_n$. The only other nonzero integers to be considered are 1 and -1. But both 1 and -1 are in the prescribed form where there are no primes in the product.

An alternative method for obtaining uniqueness (rather than ignoring the order of the factors) is to insist on a certain order of the factors. Let a be a nonzero integer. Collect the common terms and express their product by using exponents. Put the "small" primes first. Then a can be expressed as

$$a = (\pm 1)p_1^{n_1} p_2^{n_2} \cdots p_s^{n_s}$$

where $p_1, p_2, \ldots, p_s$ are primes such that $p_1 < p_2 < \cdots < p_s$ and $n_1, n_2, \ldots, n_s$ are nonnegative integers. When a is expressed in this manner, one says that a is expressed in *standard form* as a product of primes.

Let a, b be nonzero integers. By using zero exponents, if necessary, one can express a and b in standard form as products of exactly the *same* primes. Let

$$a = (\pm 1)p_1^{n_1} p_2^{n_2} \cdots p_t^{n_t} \quad \text{and} \quad b = (\pm 1)p_1^{m_1} p_2^{m_2} \cdots p_t^{m_t}.$$

If for each i ($1 \leq i \leq t$), k_i is the minimum of n_i and m_i, and r_i is the maximum of n_i and m_i, then the g.c.d. of a and b is $p_1^{k_1} p_2^{k_2} \cdots p_t^{k_t}$, and the l.c.m. of a and b is $p_1^{r_1} p_2^{r_2} \cdots p_t^{r_t}$. For instance, if $a = 1400$ and $b = 990$, then $a = 2^3 \cdot 5^2 \cdot 7$ and $b = 2 \cdot 3^2 \cdot 5 \cdot 11$ when they are expressed in standard form. Thus we can write

$$a = 2^3 \cdot 3^0 \cdot 5^2 \cdot 7^1 \cdot 11^0 \quad \text{and} \quad b = 2^1 \cdot 3^2 \cdot 5^1 \cdot 7^0 \cdot 11^1.$$

Hence the g.c.d. of a and b is $2 \cdot 5 = 10$, and the l.c.m. of a and b is $2^3 \cdot 3^2 \cdot 5^2 \cdot 7^1 \cdot 11^1 = 138{,}600$. This method of finding the g.c.d. of two nonzero integers does not provide the information necessary for writing the g.c.d. of two nonzero integers as a linear combination of them.

ADDITIONAL REFERENCES FOR CHAPTER 4

DAVENPORT, H., *The Higher Arithmetic*, London: Hutchinson's University Library (1952).

HARDY, G. H. and E. M. WRIGHT, *An Introduction to the Theory of Numbers*, Fourth Edition, Oxford: Clarendon Press (1960).

McCOY, NEAL H., *Introduction to Modern Algebra*, Boston: Allyn and Bacon, Inc. (1960).

McCOY, NEAL H., *The Theory of Numbers*, New York: The Macmillan Company (1965).

NIVEN, IVAN and HERBERT S. ZUCKERMAN, *An Introduction to the Theory of Numbers*, Second Edition, New York: John Wiley and Sons, Inc. (1966).

CHAPTER 5

INTEGRAL DOMAINS AND FIELDS

In this chapter we study two special types of rings—namely, integral domains and fields. These two algebraic systems are important because our usual "arithmetic" is carried out in either an integral domain or a field. After defining these special rings and establishing a few simple properties, we will carry out an extremely important construction in Section 3. In Section 4, we define ordered integral domains and develop some of their rudimentary properties. Then, in Section 5, we discuss the field of rational numbers and prove in particular that the field of rational numbers is ordered.

5.1 DEFINITIONS

If a is a nonzero element of a ring R such that $ab = 0$ for some nonzero element $b \in R$, then a is called a *zero divisor*. In this case b is also a zero divisor; hence, zero divisors come in pairs. Whenever two nonzero elements are multiplied together to produce zero, we have zero divisors. A commutative ring with unity element which has no zero divisors is called an *integral domain*. More formally, we make the following definition.

> **5.1.1 Definition.** *An **integral domain** is a commutative ring R with unity element which has more than one element and such that the following condition holds:*
>
> *If $r, s \in R$, $r \neq 0$, and $s \neq 0$, then $rs \neq 0$.*

An equivalent formulation of the above condition is the following:

> *If $r, s \in R$ and $rs = 0$, then $r = 0$ or $s = 0$.*

To see that these conditions are equivalent, one simply notices that one is the contrapositive of the other.

By requiring that an integral domain have more than one element, we are simply requiring that integral domains have at least one nonzero element. Note that, by exercise 6 in Section 3.3.1, the unity element of an integral domain is nonzero. Other authors may vary somewhat in their definition of integral domain; that is, not all authors require that integral domains be commutative or have a unity element.

Next we prove a theorem which provides us with a condition that can be used in the definition above.

5.1.2 Theorem. *Let R be a ring. The following are equivalent.*

1) *If $r, s \in R$ and $rs = 0$, then $r = 0$ or $s = 0$.*

2) *If $a, b, c \in R$, $c \neq 0$, and $ac = bc$, then $a = b$.*

Condition (2) is the *cancellation law of multiplication.* Notice that only *nonzero* elements can be "cancelled."

Proof. First we prove that (1) implies (2). Suppose (1) holds and let a, b, c be elements of R such that $c \neq 0$ and $ac = bc$. Then $ac - bc = 0$, and so, by the distributive law, $(a - b)c = 0$. Since $c \neq 0$, (1) implies that $a - b = 0$. Hence $a = b$. Thus (2) holds.

Now we prove that (2) implies (1). Suppose (2) holds, and let r, s be elements of R such that $rs = 0$. Suppose $r \neq 0$; then we must prove that $s = 0$. Note that $r0 = 0$ so that $rs = r0$. Since $r \neq 0$, (2) implies that $s = 0$. Hence (1) holds.

The name "integral domain" seems to imply that the notion of integral domain is a generalization of the ring of integers. And, as is easily checked, the ring of integers is an integral domain. Exercise 2 in Section 5.2.4 shows that the ring M of 2×2 matrices over I is not an integral domain. The ring $I/(6)$ of integers modulo 6 is not an integral domain since $[3] \neq [0]$, $[2] \neq [0]$, but $[3] \cdot [2] = [0]$ in $I/(6)$. On the other hand, a glance at the multiplication table of the ring $I/(7)$ of integers modulo 7 shows that $I/(7)$ is an integral domain. Theorem 5.2.2 will determine those integers n for which $I/(n)$ is an integral domain.

5.1.3 Definition. *A field is a commutative ring R with unity which has more than one element and such that every nonzero element of R has a multiplicative inverse in R.*

In other words, a field is a commutative division ring with more than one element. If one considers multiplication by multiplicative inverses as division, then a field is simply a commutative ring with unity element which has more than one element in which it is permissible to divide by nonzero elements. Recall that we have proved (Theorem 3.2.2) that the multiplicative inverse of each nonzero element of a field is unique. We denote the multiplicative inverse of $a \in R$ by a^{-1}.

There are many familiar examples of fields. For instance, the rational numbers, the real numbers, and the complex numbers are all fields; consequently, we have had experience with certain fields. Theorem 5.2.2 in the next section provides us with an infinite number of examples of fields.

5.2 SIMPLE PROPERTIES

The first theorem will show the relationship between fields and integral domains.

5.2.1 Theorem. *Every field is an integral domain. However, there exist integral domains which are not fields.*

Proof. Let F be a field. Then F is a commutative ring with unity element; in order to show that F is an integral domain, it is sufficient to show that F has no zero divisors. Let $r, s \in F$ such that $r \neq 0$ and $rs = 0$. Since $r \neq 0$ and F is a field, we know r^{-1} belongs to F. Then

$$0 = r^{-1}0 = r^{-1}(rs) = (r^{-1}r)s = es = s.$$

Hence $s = 0$, so that F has no zero divisors.

That the second part of the theorem is true can be seen by considering the ring I of integers; I is an integral domain, but not a field, since the only elements which have multiplicative inverses are 1 and -1.

For a moment, consider only the nonzero elements of a field F, and ignore the addition of the ring; i.e., we are considering the set F^* of nonzero elements of F with the binary operation multiplication. Since F has more than one element, by 3.3.1, Exercise 6, we know that the unity element of F is in F^*. Hence F^* is not empty. Theorem 5.2.1 shows that F^* is closed under multiplication. Moreover, since F is a ring, the multiplication is an associative operation on F^*. We have already noted that F^* contains an identity—namely, the unity element of F. Each nonzero element of F— that is, each element of F^*—has an inverse in F^* since F is a field. Thus F^* is a group. Since F is a commutative ring, F^* is an abelian group. Consequently, we can now state an alternative definition of field similar to the alternative definition of ring given in Section 3.1.

5.2.2 Definition (alternative). *A field is a set F containing more than one element on which there are defined two binary operations $+$ and $\cdot$ such that*

1) *F is an abelian group with respect to $+$,*

2) *F^* is an abelian group with respect to $\cdot$, and*

3) *$\cdot$ is left- and right-distributive over $+$.*

In Section 3.3, we proved that $I/(n)$ is a commutative ring with unity element for all positive integers n. The following theorem provides more specific information about $I/(n)$. In order to avoid confusion, we return to the practice of denoting elements of $I/(n)$ by $[k]$ where $[k]$ represents the equivalence class of k determined by the equivalence relation: $a \equiv b \pmod{n}$ if $a - b$ is a multiple of n.

5.2.3 Theorem. *The ring $I/(n)$ is a field if and only if n is a prime integer.*

Proof. First suppose that n is a prime integer. We must show that every nonzero $[k]$ in $I/(n)$ has a multiplicative inverse in $I/(n)$. Let $[k]$ be a nonzero element of $I/(n)$. Then k is not a multiple of n. Thus, since n is a prime integer, k and n are relatively prime. Hence there exist integers r, s such that $1 = rk + sn$, Therefore,

$$\begin{aligned}[1] &= [rk + sn]\\ &= [rk] + [sn]\\ &= [r][k] + [s][n].\end{aligned}$$

But $[n] = [0]$, so that $[1] = [r][k]$. Since $I/(n)$ is commutative, this shows that $[r]$ is the multiplicative inverse of $[k]$. Hence $I/(n)$ is a field.

Next we prove that if n is a prime integer, then $I/(n)$ is not a field. In fact, we will prove something even stronger—namely, that if n is not a prime, then $I/(n)$ is not an integral domain (and hence cannot be a field, by Theorem 5.2.1). Suppose n is not a prime integer. Then n can be written as

$$n = n_1 n_2, \qquad \text{where} \qquad 1 < n_1 < n \qquad \text{and} \qquad 1 < n_2 < n.$$

Then neither n_1 nor n_2 is a multiple of n. Hence $[n_1] \neq [0]$ and $[n_2] \neq [0]$. However,

$$[n] = [n_1 n_2] = [n_1][n_2] = [0].$$

Therefore $I/(n)$ is not an integral domain since $[n_1]$ and $[n_2]$ are zero divisors.

We have just seen that the condition "R is a field" is stronger than "R is an integral domain." However, the following theorem shows that if R is finite, these conditions are the same.

5.2.4 Theorem. *Every finite integral domain is a field.*

Proof. Let R be a finite integral domain. Let b be a nonzero element of R. We wish to show that b has a multiplicative inverse in R. Let

$$S = \{a_1, a_2, \ldots, a_n\}$$

denote the set of all nonzero elements of R. Consider the set

$$S' = \{ba_1, ba_2, \ldots, ba_n\}.$$

Since R is an integral domain, the product of nonzero elements is a nonzero element. Hence $S' \subseteq S$. Moreover, the elements of S' are distinct because if $ba_i = ba_j$ for $i \neq j$, by the cancellation law of multiplication, $a_i = a_j$. Hence S' and S each have n elements. Therefore $S' = S$. Since R has a unity element e and since $e \neq 0$, we know that $e \in S$. Hence $e \in S'$. Thus $e = ba_s$ for some $a_s \in S$. Thus a_s is the multiplicative inverse of b. Since b is an arbitrary nonzero element of R, then R is a field.

5.2.5 Exercises

1. In the ring $I/(6)$ of integers modulo 6, give an example that shows that the cancellation law of multiplication does not hold.

2. Prove that the ring M of 2×2 matrices over I is not an integral domain; i.e., find two nonzero matrices whose product is zero.

3. Let M denote the ring of 2×2 matrices over I. Find four elements of M which have multiplicative inverses in M. Are there more?

4. Given that r, s are elements of a field F and $r \neq 0$, show that there exist elements $x, y \in F$ such that $rx = s$ and $yr = s$.

5. Find the multiplicative inverse of the following elements in the field listed.

   a) $[5]$ in $I/(11)$ b) $[3]$ in $I/(7)$ c) $[19]$ in $I/(53)$ d) $[112]$ in $I/(2311)$

6. Let R be a commutative ring with unity element. If an element c of R has a multiplicative inverse, then c is called a *unit*. (Do not confuse this with unity element.)

   a) Find the units of $I/(6)$; of $I/(24)$.
   b) Which elements of $I/(n)$ will be units? Prove your answer.
   c) Prove that the set of units of a commutative ring with unity forms an abelian group under multiplication.

7. Recall the ring C of continuous functions on $[0, 1]$ of Example 6, Section 3.3. Prove or disprove that C is an integral domain.

8. Prove that the only ideals of a field F are (0) and F itself.

9. Show that if F is a field and α is a homomorphism from F to any ring, then α is either an isomorphism or $\alpha(f) = 0$ for all $f \in F$. Hint: Use Exercise 8.

5.3 THE FIELD OF QUOTIENTS OF AN INTEGRAL DOMAIN

We now turn to a different consideration. A problem quite often studied in modern algebra is this: Given an algebraic structure A which does not have a certain property P, can one construct another algebraic structure B such that B contains A and such that B does have property P? We are going to consider this problem in one specific case. If D is a given integral domain, then the nonzero elements of D may or may nor have multiplicative inverses in D. We want to construct an algebraic system F which will contain D and which will have the property that all its nonzero elements have multiplicative inverses in F; i.e., we want to construct a field F which contains the integral domain D. The field F is called the *field of quotients* of the integral domain D.

In particular, if we start with the integral domain I of all integers, the field of quotients of I is simply the field of rational numbers. In a later section we will develop some specific properties of the rational numbers. However, now we are interested only in their construction.

In the construction of the field of quotients of an integral domain D, one can make use of previous experience with the field of rational numbers. Hence, before constructing the field of quotients of D, one will find it helpful to consider the following heuristic description of the construction. A rigorous argument will follow it. The heuristic discussion is based on our previous knowledge of the field of rational numbers.

Heuristic description. Let D be a given integral domain. The field of quotients F of D will be all "fractions" a/b where $a, b \in D, b \neq 0$. (We will have to give a precise definition of "fraction" in the actual construction.) These fractions must have the property $a/b = ac/bc$ for all $a, b, c \in D$, $b \neq 0, c \neq 0$. For $a/b, c/d \in F$ (that is, $a, b, c, d \in D, b \neq 0, d \neq 0$), we will define

$$\frac{a}{b} + \frac{c}{d} = \frac{ad + bc}{bd} \quad \text{and} \quad \frac{a}{b} \cdot \frac{c}{d} = \frac{ac}{bd}.$$

Then F is a field with these definitions of addition and multiplication. Moreover, if one thinks of elements d of D as "fractions" of the form $d/1$, then D is contained in F.

The field of quotients of an integral domain. Let D be an integral domain. Let

$$E = \{(a, b) \mid a, b \in D, b \neq 0\};$$

that is, E is a set of ordered pairs of elements of D where the second element is not zero. (These ordered pairs (a, b) are not quite the "fractions" we want since $(a, b) \neq (ax, bx)$ if $x \neq 1$). On E define a relation by

$$(a, b) \sim (c, d) \quad \text{if and only if} \quad ad = bc$$

for all $(a, b), (c, d) \in E$.

5.3.1 Theorem. $\sim$ *is an equivalence relation on* E.

Proof. Let $(a, b), (c, d), (f, g) \in E$.

1) $(a, b) \sim (a, b)$ since $ab = ab$. Therefore $\sim$ is reflexive.

2) Suppose $(a, b) \sim (c, d)$. Then $ad = bc$. Thus, since R is commutative, $da = cb$. Hence $(c, d) \sim (a, b)$, and so $\sim$ is symmetric.

3) Suppose $(a, b) \sim (c, d)$ and $(c, d) \sim (f, g)$. Then $ad = bc$ and $cg = df$. Multiplying the first equation by g and the second by b, we get $adg = bcg$ and $cgb = dfb$. From these last two equations, we get $adg = dfb$; that is, $(ag)d = (bf)d$. Since $(c, d) \in E, d \neq 0$. Since D is an integral domain, the cancellation law of multiplication holds, so d can be cancelled to give $ag = bf$. Hence $(a, b) \sim (f, g)$, proving that $\sim$ is transitive. Hence $\sim$ is an equivalence relation.

We denote the equivalence classes of $(a, b) \in E$ by $[a, b]$ rather than $[(a, b)]$. Then

$$[a, b] = \{(c, d) \in E \mid (c, d) \sim (a, b)\} = \{(c, d) \in E \mid ad = bc\}.$$

Therefore, two equivalence classes $[a, b]$ and $[c, d]$ are equal if $(a, b) \sim (c, d)$; i.e., if $ad = bc$. Hence $[a, b] = [ax, bx]$ for all nonzero $x \in D$. Thus, if one considers the equivalence classes $[a, b]$ as the "fractions" described above, they have the property which was insisted on in the heuristic description—namely, $[a, b] = [ax, bx]$ for all $(a, b) \in E$ and all nonzero $x \in D$.

Let F be the collection of all equivalence classes of $\sim$ on E. Then F is the collection of all "fractions" $[a, b]$ where $a, b \in D$, $b \neq 0$. Define addition and multiplication on F by

$$[a, b] + [c, d] = [ad + bc, bd]$$

and

$$[a, b][c, d] = [ac, bd]$$

for all $[a, b], [c, d] \in F$.

As before, when we have defined operations on equivalence classes, we must prove that these operations are well defined.

5.3.2 Theorem. *The addition and multiplication defined above are well defined.*

Proof. We consider the addition and leave the multiplication as an exercise. Suppose that $[a, b] = [a_1, b_1]$ and $[c, d] = [c_1, d_1]$. Then $ab_1 = ba_1$ and $cd_1 = dc_1$. Multiplying the first equation by dd_1 and the second by bb_1, we get

(1) $$adb_1d_1 = a_1d_1bd$$

and

(2) $$bcb_1d_1 = b_1c_1bd.$$

Therefore

$$(ad + bc)b_1d_1 = (a_1d_1 + b_1c_1)bd,$$

proving that

$$[ad + bc, bd] = [a_1d_1 + b_1c_1, b_1d_1].$$

Hence

$$[a, b] + [c, d] = [a_1, b_1] + [c_1, d_1].$$

5.3.3 Theorem. *F is a field with the addition and multiplication defined above.*

Proof. It is a routine matter to show that F is an abelian group with respect to addition. The zero is $[0, x]$ for any nonzero $x \in D$, and the negative of $[a, b]$ is $[-a, b]$. The details are left as an exercise.

Similarly, the associativity and commutativity of multiplication are left as exercises.

Since the multiplication is commutative, we need verify only one distributive law:

$$\begin{aligned}
[a, b]([c, d] + [f, g]) &= [a, b][cg + df, dg] \\
&= [acg + adf, bdg] \\
&= [acgb + adfb, b^2dg] \\
&= [ac, bd] + [af, bg] \\
&= [a, b][c, d] + [a, b][f, g].
\end{aligned}$$

Thus F is a commutative ring. Furthermore, F has a unity element $[x, x]$ where x is any nonzero element of D; i.e., the unity element of F is the equivalence class which has identical nonzero elements in the first and second places. Note that $[x, x] = [y, y]$ for all nonzero $x, y \in D$. To verify that $[x, x]$ is the unity element of F, we need only to observe that

$$[a, b][x, x] = [ax, bx] = [a, b].$$

To complete the proof that F is a field, we must show that every nonzero element of F has an inverse. Let $[m, n]$ be a nonzero element of F. Then $m, n \in D$ and $n \neq 0$. Moreover, since $[m, n]$ is nonzero, $m \neq 0$. Then $[n, m]$ is also an element of F and, in fact,

$$[m, n][n, m] = [mn, mn]$$

and $[mn, mn]$ is the unity element of F. Hence the multiplicative inverse of $[m, n]$ is $[n, m]$. (In terms of "fractions," this says that the inverse of m/n is n/m.)

The original problem posed at the beginning of this section was the following: Given an integral domain D, construct a field F *containing* D. We have constructed a field—the field of quotients of D; but does it contain D? Definitely not! The field F consists of equivalence classes of ordered pairs of elements of D. However, F does contain a subring which is isomorphic to D. The next theorem will prove just that. When F contains a subring isomorphic to D, one says that D is *embedded* in F. If we identify the elements of D with their image in F under the isomorphism, then F does contain D. In the context of "fractions," the subring of F will be all fractions of the form $d/1$; i.e., we will consider the elements of D as "fractions with denominator 1."

5.3.4 Theorem. *The field F contains a subring R which is isomorphic to D.*

Proof. Let $R = \{[a, 1] \mid a \in D\}$. We must show that R is a subring of F. Let $[a, 1], [b, 1] \in R$. Then

$$[a, 1] + [b, 1] = [a + b, 1] \in R,$$

and the additive inverse $[-a, 1]$ of $[a, 1]$ belongs to R. Furthermore, $[a, 1][b, 1] = [ab, 1] \in R$. Therefore, by Theorem 3.5.2, R is a subring of F.

To prove that D is isomorphic to R, we must define a mapping α from D to R and prove that α is an isomorphism. Define α by $\alpha(d) = [d, 1]$ for all $d \in D$ (that is, d corresponds to $d/1$). Clearly α is a well-defined mapping. First we show that α is a (ring) homomorphism. Let $c, d \in D$. Then

$$\alpha(c + d) = [c + d, 1] = [c, 1] + [d, 1] = \alpha(c) + \alpha(d),$$

and similarly,

$$\alpha(cd) = \alpha(c)\,\alpha(d).$$

Let $[d, 1] \in R$. Then $d \in D$ and $\alpha(d) = [d, 1]$. Hence α is onto. Now suppose $\alpha(d) = \alpha(c)$. Then $[d, 1] = [c, 1]$. Hence $(d, 1) \sim (c, 1)$, and so $d \cdot 1 = c \cdot 1$. Thus $d = c$, and so α is one-to-one. This completes the proof.

For every $[a, b] \in F$, observe that

$$[a, b] = [a, 1][1, b] = [a, 1][b, 1]^{-1}.$$

If we identify elements of F and D by the isomorphism above, we see that every element $[a, b]$ of F can be written

$$[a, b] = ab^{-1}.$$

Hence we obtain the "fractions" we desired.

5.3.5 Exercises

1. Explain why it is necessary to use the equivalence relation on E and to consider equivalence classes rather than the ordered pairs of E.

2. Prove that the multiplication on F is well defined.

3. Let D be an integral domain. Let $\sim$, E, and F be defined as in the previous discussion. Define an operation $\oplus$ on F by $[a, b] \oplus [c, d] = [a + c, b + d]$ for all $[a, b], [c, d] \in F$. Prove or disprove that $\oplus$ is well defined.

4. Prove that F is an abelian group with respect to addition.

5. The zero of F is $[0, x]$ for any nonzero $x \in D$. How can this be true when we have proved that the zero of a ring is unique?

6. Let R be a ring which may or may not have a unity element. The purpose of this exercise is to construct a ring S which does have a unity element such that R can be embedded in S. Let $S = \{(n, r) \mid n \in I, r \in R\}$ where I denotes the ring of integers; i.e., S consists of ordered pairs (n, r) where n is an integer and r is an element of R. We make the following definition of $=$, $+$, and $\cdot$.

$$(n, r) = (m, s) \text{ if } n = m \text{ and } r = s,$$
$$(n, r) + (m, s) = (n + m, r + s),$$

and

$$(n, r) \cdot (m, s) = (nm, ms + ns + rs)$$

for all (n, r), $(m, s) \in S$. Notice that, since m is an integer, mr means r added to itself m times. Hence $mr \in R$. Similarly, $ns \in R$, so that $mr + ns + rs \in R$. Hence $(nm, mr + ns + rs) \in S$.

a) Prove that S is a ring.
b) Prove that S has a unity element.
c) Prove that R can be embedded in S; i.e., show that S contains a subring of R which is isomorphic to R.

The solution of this exercise is a proof of the following theorem.

5.3.6 Theorem. *Every ring can be embedded in a ring with unity element.*

7. We have seen that $I/(5)$ is an integral domain. Write out explicitly the elements of the field of quotients of $I/(5)$. Show that the field of quotients of $I/(5)$ is simply $I/(5)$.

8. Prove that the field of quotients F of an integral domain D is the *smallest* field containing D; i.e., show that any field containing D must also contain F.

9. Prove that the field of quotients of an integral domain D is the intersection of all fields containing D.

5.4 ORDERED INTEGRAL DOMAINS

The algebraic systems with which we are the most familiar—namely, the ring of integers, the field of rational numbers, and the field of real numbers—have an important special property which does not hold in general in algebraic systems. This property is that elements can be compared by saying one is "larger" than another. A rule which allows us to determine which of two elements is "larger" is called an *ordering*, and an algebraic system on which an ordering is defined is said to be *ordered*. When we think of the integers as points on a line,

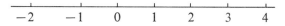

we say that $m < n$ if m is to the left of n. This is an example of an ordering on the ring of integers. Hence the ring of integers can be ordered. It should be pointed out that possibly there are other orderings which could be defined on the ring of integers; however, the one above is certainly the most natural.

Reconsidering the ordering "$m < n$ if m is to the left of n," one immediately sees that this could be restated as "$m < n$ if $n - m$ is a positive integer." This relationship between the ordering and the set of positive integers is generalized in the next definition.

5.4.1 Definition. *An integral domain D is said to be **ordered** if D contains a subset D_p which has the following properties.*

1) $ab \in D_p$ for all $a, b \in D_p$,
2) $a + b \in D_p$ for all $a, b \in D_p$, and

3) *for each element $a \in D$, exactly **one** of the following holds:* $a = 0$, $a \in D_p$, *or* $-a \in D_p$.

*The elements of D_p are called **positive** elements, and the nonzero elements of D which are not in D_p are called **negative** elements.*

The properties (1) and (2) simply state that D_p is closed under addition and multiplication. Property (3) is often called the *trichotomy law*. If an ordered integral domain is also a field, then it is called an *ordered field*.

It is easy to see that the integers form an ordered integral domain. The set I_p of positive elements are those to the right of zero on the number line. Later we will prove in detail that the field of rational numbers is an ordered field.

If D is an ordered integral domain with set of positive elements D_p, then for $x, y \in D$, we define

$$x < y \qquad \text{if} \qquad y - x \in D_p.$$

In this case we say "x is less than y" or "y is greater than x." Note that $a > 0$ means $a \in D_p$. Hence $a > 0$ means that a is a positive element. Similarly $a < 0$ means that a is a negative element. Using this notation, we can restate Definition 5.4.1 as follows.

5.4.2 Definition (alternative). *An integral domain D is an **ordered integral domain** if there is defined on D a relation $<$ such that*

1) *if $a > 0$ and $b > 0$, then $ab > 0$,*

2) *if $a > 0$ and $b > 0$, then $a + b > 0$, and*

3) *for all $a \in D$, exactly **one** of the following is true:* $a = 0$, $a > 0$, *or* $a < 0$.

Now it is easy to prove that the relation $<$ on an ordered integral domain D has the usual properties of inequalities.

5.4.3 Theorem. *Let D be an ordered integral domain, and let $a, b, c \in D$.*

1) *If $a > b$, then $a + c > b + c$ for all $c \in D$.*

2) *If $a > b$ and $c > 0$, then $ac > bc$.*

3) *If $a > b$ and $c < 0$, then $ac < bc$.*

4) *If $a > b$ and $b > c$, then $a > c$.*

5) *If $a \neq 0$, then $a^2 > 0$.*

Proof. (1), (2), and (5) will be proved here, and (3) and (4) will be left as exercises. In (1), since $a > b$, then $a - b > 0$. Hence

$$a + (c - c) - b = a + c - (b + c) > 0.$$

Thus

$$a + c > b + c.$$

To prove (2), note that $a > b$ means that $a - b > 0$. Hence, by Definition 5.4.2, part (1), $(a - b)c > 0$. Thus

$$ac - bc > 0,$$

so that $ac > bc$.

Now assume that $a \neq 0$. By the trichotomy law of ordered integral domains, either $a > 0$ or $a < 0$. If $a > 0$, then $a^2 > 0$, by 5.4.2, part (1). If $a < 0$, then $-a > 0$. Hence, by 5.4.2, part (1), $(-a)(-a) > 0$. But $(-a)(-a) = aa = a^2$, by Theorem 2.2.4. Hence, in either case $a^2 > 0$.

5.4.4 Exercises

1. Prove Theorem 5.4.3, parts (3) and (4).

2. Let u, v, x, y be elements of an ordered integral domain D. Prove the following propositions.

   a) If $u > x$, then $-u < -x$.
   b) If $u > v$ and $x > y$, then $u + x > v + y$.
   c) If $uv > ux$ and $u > 0$, then $v > x$.

3. Let a be an element of an ordered integral domain. Define $|a|$, called "absolute value of a," as follows:

$$|a| = \begin{cases} a & \text{if } a \geq 0. \\ -a & \text{if } a < 0. \end{cases}$$

Here $a \geq 0$ means $a > 0$ or $a = 0$. Prove the following propositions for elements $a, b \in D$.

   a) $|ab| = |a|\,|b|$.
   b) $-|a| \leq a \leq |a|$.
   c) $|a + b| \leq |a| + |b|$.

5.5 THE FIELD OF RATIONAL NUMBERS

In Section 5.3 we constructed the field of quotients of an integral domain and remarked that the field of quotients of the integral domain of integers is the field of rational numbers. The symbol Q will be used to denote the field of rational numbers. By our construction in Section 5.3, Q is the set of all equivalence classes $[a, b]$ where $a, b \in I$ and $b \neq 0$. If we denote this equivalence class $[a, b]$ by a/b, then by transcribing the definitions of Section 5.3, we see that Q is the set of all "fractions" a/b where $a, b \in I$, $b \neq 0$ such that

$$\frac{a}{b} = \frac{c}{d} \quad \text{if} \quad ad = bc,$$

$$\frac{a}{b} + \frac{c}{d} = \frac{ad + bc}{bd},$$

and

$$\frac{a}{b} \cdot \frac{c}{d} = \frac{ac}{bd}$$

for all a/b, $c/d \in Q$.

Notice that $(-a)/b = a/(-b)$ since $(-a)(-b) = ab$. Hence every rational number can be expressed as a/b where a, $b \in I$ and $b > 0$. Moreover, if a, b have a common factor c such that $a = ca_1$ and $b = cb_1$, then $a/b = ca_1/cb_1 = a_1/b_1$. Consequently, every rational number can be expressed as a/b where a, $b \in I$, $b > 0$, and a and b have no factors in common. When rational numbers are expressed in this manner, one says that they are in *reduced form*.

In Section 5.4 it was established that the ring I of integers was an ordered integral domain. Let $<$ denote the ordering on I. This ordering is used to induce an ordering on the field of rational numbers.

5.5.1 Theorem. Q *is an ordered field. In fact, the set Q_p of positive elements of Q is precisely the set of rational numbers a/b such that $ab > 0$.*

Proof. First note that ab is an integer, so that $ab > 0$ simply means that ab is a positive integer. Here we are using the ordering on I. We must verify that Q_p has the properties of Definition 5.4.2.

Let a/b and $c/d \in Q$. Then a, b, c, $d \in I$ and $b > 0$ and $d > 0$. If a/b and c/d are elements of Q_p, then $ab > 0$ and $cd > 0$. We want to show that

$$\frac{a}{b} + \frac{c}{d} = \frac{ad + bc}{bd} \in Q_p;$$

that is, that

$$bd(ad + bc) = abd^2 + cdb^2 > 0.$$

Since $ab > 0$ and $d^2 > 0$, the ordering on I implies that $abd^2 > 0$. Similarly $cdb^2 > 0$, so that $abd^2 + cdb^2 > 0$. Furthermore, $ac/bd \in Q_p$ since $acbd = abcd > 0$ because $ab > 0$ and $cd > 0$. If a/b is a nonzero element of Q, then $a \neq 0$. Hence $ab \neq 0$ since $b \neq 0$. By the trichotomy law of the ordering on I, either $ab > 0$ or $ab < 0$. Thus $a/b \in Q_p$ or $-a/b \in Q_p$. Hence the trichotomy law holds for Q_p. Thus Q is an ordered field with set of positive elements Q_p.

Thus, for two rational numbers a/b and c/d, $a/b > c/d$ if and only if

$$\frac{ad - bc}{bd} \in Q_p;$$

that is, $a/b > c/d$ if and only if $bd(ad - bc) > 0$. If we assume that a/b and c/d are in reduced form, then $b > 0$ and $d > 0$, so $bd > 0$. Hence $ad - bc > 0$. Consequently, we see that

$$a/b > c/d \qquad \text{if and only if} \qquad ad > bc.$$

Two additional properties of the field of rational numbers are made specific by the next two theorems. Theorem 5.5.3 is called the *Archimedean Property*.

5.5.2 Theorem. *Between any two distinct rational numbers, there is another rational number. In particular, if u, v are rational numbers such that u < v, then*

$$u < \frac{u+v}{2} < v.$$

Proof. Since $u < v$, then $u + u < u + v$, by 5.4.3, part (1). (Here use is being made of the fact that Q is an ordered field.) Hence $2u < u + v$. By multiplying both sides by the positive rational number $1/2$, we get that

$$u < \frac{u+v}{2}.$$

Similarly, one can show that

$$\frac{u+v}{2} < v,$$

which completes the proof of the theorem.

5.5.3 Theorem (Archimedean Property). *If u, v are any positive rational numbers, then there exists a positive integer n such that nu > v.*

Proof. Let $u = a/b$ and $v = c/d$ where a, b, c, d are all positive integers. Let $n = 2bc$. We must show that $2bc(a/b) > c/d$. But this is true if $2ad > 1$; and $a > 0$ and $d > 0$ clearly imply that $2ad > 1$.

This section on the rational numbers is concluded by providing an example of a "number" which is not a rational number.

5.5.4 Theorem. *The number $\sqrt{2}$ is not a rational number.*

Proof. By $\sqrt{2}$ we mean the unique positive real number r such that $r^2 = 2$. That $\sqrt{2}$ is not a rational number is proved by contradiction. Assume that $\sqrt{2}$ is a rational number; say $\sqrt{2} = p/q$. Without loss of generality, p/q can be taken to be in *reduced form*; i.e., $q > 0$ and p and q have no factors in common. Since $\sqrt{2} = p/q$, then $2 = p^2/q^2$, and so $2q^2 = p^2$. Thus $2 \mid p^2$ and, by Theorem 4.2.7, $2 \mid p$. Thus $p = 2t$ for some integer t. Then $p^2 = 4t^2$, and so $2q^2 = 4t^2$. By the cancellation law of multiplication (I is an integral domain), $q^2 = 2t^2$. But this implies that q has a factor of 2. Hence p and q each have a factor of 2, contrary to our assumption that p/q is in reduced form. Hence $\sqrt{2}$ is not a rational number.

5.5.5 Exercises

1. Given that r, s are positive rational numbers such that $r < s$, prove that $1/s < 1/r$.

2. Given that r, s are rational numbers such that $r < s$, and given that u, v are positive rational numbers, prove that

$$r < \frac{ur + vs}{u + v} < s.$$

3. Given that r, s are rational numbers such that $r < s$, and given that n is any integer, show that there exist rational numbers $t_1, t_2, \ldots, t_n$ such that

$$r < t_1 < t_2 < \cdots < t_n < s.$$

4. Prove that $\sqrt{5}$ is not a rational number. Can you generalize?

5. Prove or disprove that Q_p is well ordered; i.e., prove or disprove that every nonempty subset of Q_p has a least element.

6. Is this a true statement: $\frac{2}{3} = \frac{10}{15}$? Why?

ADDITIONAL REFERENCES FOR CHAPTER 5

BARNES, WILFRED E., *Introduction to Abstract Algebra*, Boston: Heath and Company (1963).

HERSTEIN, I. N., *Topics in Algebra*, New York: Blaisdell (1964).

McCoy, NEAL H., *Introduction to Modern Algebra*, Boston: Allyn and Bacon (1960).

WHITESITT, J. ELDON, *Principles of Modern Algebra*, Reading, Massachusetts: Addison-Wesley (1964).

CHAPTER 6

POLYNOMIALS

6.1 DEFINITION OF POLYNOMIALS

Polynomials represent an area of mathematics with which everyone is familiar. As early as junior high, polynomials are introduced and considerable amounts of time are devoted to becoming familiar with them. We learn to add them, multiply them, factor them, and simplify them. Later on, at the advanced senior high level or beginning college level, polynomials appear in a quite different way. In calculus and precalculus courses, we view polynomials as functions and are concerned with their continuity, their derivatives, their integrals, and their maxima and minima.

Here we will be interested in polynomials from still another viewpoint. First, we must define carefully what a polynomial really is. Then we construct a "ring of polynomials" and study the algebraic properties of polynomials as elements of this ring. This study of polynomials is essential to understanding many concepts in a more thorough study of modern algebra. Polynomials are extremely useful in the study of rings and fields. On the other hand, the material presented here is important to those who plan to teach mathematics at the junior or senior high level. Indeed, having a basic understanding of polynomials is mandatory for someone who will teach about polynomials.

In this chapter we will define polynomials which have coefficients in a commutative ring with unity. Later on it will become necessary to restrict the generality of the ring in order to obtain usable and "nice" results. The restriction will be to require that the ring be an integral domain or a field. Finally, we further restrict the situation by proving several specific results concerning polynomials over the field of rational numbers. In several examples and exercises in this chapter, a basic familiarity of the fields of real numbers and complex numbers has been assumed.

Let R be a commutative ring with unity element which we denote by 1. Let x be a symbol which is not an element of R. The symbol x is not considered (for the present anyway) as an element of any algebraic system; it is just a symbol which we will use in an entirely formal way. Such a symbol is customarily called an *indeterminate*. In the discussion to follow, we will construct a ring which contains both R and x.

Our definition of polynomial is motivated by the place value system used in ordinary arithmetic; for instance, $235 = 2 \cdot 10^2 + 3 \cdot 10^1 + 5 \cdot 10^0$. Here the 10's simply indicate in which place the 2, 3, and 5 should go.

103

6.1.1 Definition. *Let R be a commutative ring with unity element and let x be an indeterminate. A symbol of the form*

$$a_0x^0 * a_1x^1 * a_2x^2 * \cdots * a_nx^n$$

where $a_0, a_1, a_2, \ldots, a_n \in R$ and n is a nonnegative integer is called a **polynomial in x with coefficients in R.** *For $0 \le i \le n$, a_i is called the* **coefficient** *of x^i and a_ix^i is the* **term** *with coefficient a_i.*

The x's here are simply place holders. One *must not* think of x^i as x multiplied by itself i times; for after all, x does not belong to any ring, so no multiplication is defined for x. Moreover a_ix^i is not the product of a_i and x^i since such a product is not defined. The symbol $*$ between the terms of a polynomial is merely a means of spacing the terms. It is often convenient to "name" polynomials. A common way of naming polynomials is this: we write

$$f(x) = a_0x^0 * a_1x^1 * \cdots * a_nx^n$$

where $a_0, a_1, \ldots, a_n \in R$ and x is an indeterminate. Here $f(x)$ is the "name" of this polynomial. Do not think of $f(x)$ as a function which can be evaluated; $f(x)$ is merely a name which we use to facilitate our discussion of the polynomial $a_0x^0 * a_1x^1 * \cdots * a_nx^n$.

Later we will be able to attach some meaning to the symbols x^i and a_ix^i, but for now they must remain as formal symbols. Consequently, since x is merely a place holder, an alternate definition of polynomial could be a symbol of the form $(a_0, a_1, a_2, \ldots, a_n)$ where $a_0, a_1, a_2, \ldots, a_n \in R$ and n is a nonnegative integer. All the forthcoming discussion could be done with these symbols rather than the polynomials we have defined. However, our definition seems more natural.

6.1.2 Notation. *For a commutative ring R with unity element and an indeterminate x, let R[x] denote the set of all polynomials in x with coefficients in R.*

For the sake of an example, let R be the ring I of integers. Then the following are polynomials in an indeterminate x over I:

(a) $2x^0 * 3x^1 * (-4)x^2$,
(b) $2x^0$,
(c) $0x^0 * 3x^1 * 0x^2 * 2x^3$,
(d) $2x^0 * 0x^1 * 0x^2 * 0x^3 * 0x^4$.

For each of these polynomials, we could produce a different polynomial by writing additional terms with zero coefficients. But our past experience with polynomials tells us that adding terms with zero coefficients should not produce new polynomials. To clear up this situation, we must define precisely what is meant by the equality of polynomials.

6.1.3 Definition. *Let R be a commutative ring with unity element, and let x be an indeterminate. Let*

$$f(x) = a_0x^0 * a_1x^1 * \cdots * a_nx^n$$

and

$$g(x) = b_0x^0 * b_1x^1 * \cdots * b_mx^m$$

*be elements of $R[x]$. We say $f(x)$ **equals** $g(x)$ if $f(x)$ and $g(x)$ are identical except for terms with zero coefficients; that is $f(x) = g(x)$ if $a_i = b_i$ for all i.*

Consequently, in view of this definition, we can disregard terms with zero coefficients. Therefore, for the sake of brevity, we shall not write those terms which have zero coefficients. Hence (b) and (d) above are the same polynomial $2x^0$, and (c) is to be written as $3x^1 * 2x^3$.

With this understanding about zero coefficients, we can speak, with meaning, of the coefficient of x^i of a certain polynomial where i is any non-negative integer; e.g., the coefficient of x^{14} of the polynomial $3x^2 * (-5)x^7$ of $I[x]$ is 0.

The fact that the x's are simply place holders and the definition we have just given for equality both indicate the importance of the coefficients of a certain polynomial. Hence, when one wants to prove that two polynomials $f(x)$ and $g(x)$ are equal, it is "standard operating procedure" to prove that for all i the coefficient of x^i in $f(x)$ is the same as the coefficient of x^i in $g(x)$. Also, to define a polynomial, it is sufficient to state the coefficient of x^i for all i.

Now we define an addition and multiplication which will make $R[x]$ into a ring.

6.1.4 Definition. *Let R be a commutative ring with unity element and let x be an indeterminate. Let*

$$f(x) = a_0x^0 * a_1x^1 * \cdots * a_nx^n$$

and

$$g(x) = b_0x^0 * b_1x^1 * \cdots * b_mx^m$$

be elements of $R[x]$. Then

$$f(x) + g(x) = (a_0 + b_0)x^0 * (a_1 + b_1)x^1 * \cdots;$$

that is, the coefficient of x^i in $f(x) + g(x)$ is $a_i + b_i$, and

$$f(x)g(x) = c_0x^0 * c_1x^1 * \cdots * c_{n+m}x^{n+m}$$

where, for $i = 0, 1, \ldots, n + m$,

$$c_i = a_ib_0 + a_{i-1}b_1 + a_{i-2}b_2 + \cdots + a_1b_{i-1} + a_0b_i.$$

Recall that by our agreement concerning terms with zero coefficients, $a_k = 0$ if $k > m$, and $b_j = 0$ if $j > n$. An alternative description of the multiplication defined above is this: the coefficient of x^i in $f(x)g(x)$ is the sum of all products $a_s b_r$ where $s + r = i$.

To illustrate these definitions, let us return to $I[x]$. Let

$$f(x) = 2x^0 * (-3)x^1 * 1x^2 \quad \text{and} \quad g(x) = 2x^1 * 3x^3.$$

Then the coefficient of x^3 in $f(x)$ is 0 by our agreement, so consequently,

$$f(x) + g(x) = (2 + 0)x^0 * (-3 + 2)x^1 * (1 + 0)x^2 * (0 + 3)x^3$$
$$= 2x^0 * (-1)x^1 * 1x^2 * 3x^3.$$

Furthermore,

$$f(x)g(x) = c_0 x^0 * c_1 x^1 * c_2 x^2 * c_3 x^3 * c_4 x^4 * c_5 x^5$$

where

$c_0 = a_0 b_0 = 2 \cdot 0 = 0,$

$c_1 = a_1 b_0 + a_0 b_1 = (-3) \cdot 0 + 2 \cdot 2 = 4,$

$c_2 = a_2 b_0 + a_1 b_1 + a_0 b_2 = 2 \cdot 0 + (-3) \cdot 2 + 2 \cdot 0 = -6,$

$c_3 = a_3 b_0 + a_2 b_1 + a_1 b_2 + a_0 b_3 = 0 \cdot 0 + 1 \cdot 2 + (-3) \cdot 0 + 2 \cdot 3 = 8,$

$c_4 = a_4 b_0 + a_3 b_1 + a_2 b_2 + a_1 b_3 + a_0 b_4$
$\quad = 0 \cdot 0 + 0 \cdot 2 + 1 \cdot 0 + (-3) \cdot 3 + 2 \cdot 0 = -9,$

$c_5 = a_5 b_0 + a_4 b_1 + a_3 b_2 + a_2 b_3 + a_1 b_4 + a_0 b_5$
$\quad = 0 \cdot 0 + 0 \cdot 2 + 0 \cdot 0 + 1 \cdot 3 + (-3) \cdot 0 + 2 \cdot 0 = 3.$

Therefore $f(x)g(x) = 4x^1 * (-6)x^2 * 8x^3 * (-9)x^4 * 3x^5.$

6.1.5 Theorem. *Let R be a commutative ring with unity element, and let x be an indeterminate. Then, with the addition and multiplication defined above, $R[x]$ is a commutative ring with unity element. In particular $R[x]$ is called the **ring of polynomials with coefficients in R.***

Proof. It is evident from the definition that addition and multiplication are closed binary operations on $R[x]$. That addition is associative and commutative follows immediately from the definition and the fact that the addition in R is associative and commutative. Furthermore, the polynomial $0x^0$ is the zero of $R[x]$ since for any polynomial

$$f(x) = a_0 x^0 * a_1 x^1 * \cdots * a_n x^n \in R[x],$$

we have

$$f(x) + 0x^0 = (a_0 + 0)x^0 * a_1 x^1 * \cdots * a_n x^n = f(x).$$

Moreover, the additive inverse of $f(x)$ is

$$(-a_0)x^0 * (-a_1)x^1 * \cdots * (-a_n)x^n.$$

Hence $R[x]$ is an abelian group with respect to addition.

Now let

$$f(x) = a_0 x^0 * a_1 x^1 * \cdots * a_n x^n,$$
$$g(x) = b_0 x^0 * b_1 x^1 * \cdots * b_m x^m,$$
$$h(x) = c_0 x^0 * c_1 x^1 * \cdots * c_p x^p$$

be arbitrary elements of $R[x]$. The coefficient of x^i in $f(x)g(x)$ is

$$a_i b_0 + a_{i-1} b_1 + \cdots + a_1 b_{i-1} + a_0 b_i,$$

which, since R is a commutative ring, is equal to

$$b_i a_0 + b_{i-1} a_1 + \cdots + b_1 a_{i-1} + b_0 a_i,$$

the coefficient of x^i in $g(x)f(x)$. Hence $f(x)g(x) = g(x)f(x)$.

Next we prove that multiplication is associative. Write

$$f(x)g(x) = d_0 x^0 * d_1 x^1 * \cdots * d_{n+m} x^{n+m}.$$

Then the coefficient of x^k in $(f(x)g(x))h(x)$ is

$$d_k c_0 + d_{k-1} c_1 + \cdots + d_1 c_{k-1} + d_0 c_k$$

where, for $0 \le s \le k$,

$$d_s = a_s b_0 + a_{s-1} b_1 + \cdots + a_1 b_{s-1} + a_0 b_s.$$

Thus the coefficient of x^k in $(f(x)g(x))h(x)$ is the sum of all products of the form

$$(a_u b_v) c_w$$

where u, v, w are integers such that $u + v + w = k$, Now, on the other hand, let us write

$$g(x)h(x) = e_0 x^0 * e_1 x^1 * \cdots * e_{m+p} x^{m+p}.$$

Then the coefficient of x^k in $f(x)\big(g(x)h(x)\big)$ is

$$a_k e_0 + a_{k-1} e_1 + \cdots + a_1 e_{k-1} + a_0 e_k$$

where, for $0 \le t \le k$,

$$e_t = b_t c_0 + b_{t-1} c_1 + \cdots + b_1 c_{t-1} + b_0 c_t.$$

Therefore, the coefficient of x^k in $f(x)\big(g(x)h(x)\big)$ is the sum of all products of the form

$$a_u(b_v c_w)$$

where u, v, w are integers such that $u + v + w = k$. Hence, since multiplication in R is associative, the coefficient of x^k in $(f(x)g(x))h(x)$ and $f(x)\big(g(x)h(x)\big)$ is the same. Thus these products of polynomials are equal.

The proof of the distributive laws is left as an exercise. Also, if 1 is the unity element of R, then the polynomial $1x^0$ is the unity element of $R[x]$. The proof of this fact is left as an exercise also.

beginning of the discussion of polynomials, we stated our inten-
\struct a ring which contained both R and x—$R[x]$ is this ring.
{[x]$ does not, in a strict sense, contain R. But $R[x]$ does contain
a subring which is isomorphic to R; i.e., R can be *embedded* in $R[x]$. Also
$R[x]$ contains a polynomial which we can associate with x.

6.1.6 Theorem. *The ring $R[x]$ contains a subring R' which is isomorphic
to R.*

Proof. Let $R' = \{ax^0 \mid a \in R\}$; that is, R' is the set of polynomials in
$R[x]$ which have 0 as the coefficient of x^i for all $i > 0$. Let $ax^0, bx^0 \in R'$.
Then $(ax^0)(bx^0) = (ab)x^0$ and $ax^0 + bx^0 = (a + b)x^0$. Hence R' is
closed under addition and multiplication. Moreover, $(-a)x^0$ is an element
of R' and is the additive of ax^0. Thus R' is a subring of $R[x]$.

Define a mapping $\alpha: R' \to R$ by $\alpha(ax^0) = a$ for all $ax^0 \in R'$. We must
show that α is an isomorphism. That α is one-to-one and onto is clear. Let
$ax^0, bx^0 \in R'$. Then

$$\alpha(ax^0 + bx^0) = \alpha((a + b)x^0) = a + b = \alpha(ax^0) + \alpha(bx^0)$$

and

$$\alpha((ax^0)(bx^0)) = \alpha((ab)x^0) = ab = \alpha(ax^0)\alpha(bx^0).$$

Hence α is an isomorphism, completing the proof of the theorem.

Theorem 6.1.6 allows us to simplify our notation somewhat. Since R is
isomorphic to R', let us write the elements of R in place of those of R'. Then
the polynomial ax^0 will be denoted simply by a; i.e., we simply omit x^0 when
writing polynomials. Furthermore, if 1 is the unity element of R, write
x in place of $1x^1$ and x^i in place of $1x^i$ for $i > 1$. Then x is a polynomial
which belongs to $R[x]$. Also we will write $-ax^i$ in place of $(-a)x^i$.

With these simplifications we now have a ring $R[x]$ which contains R and
x. Since $x \in R[x]$, we consider the product of x with itself. The resulting
polynomial will be x^2. Here we compute $(0x^0 + 1x^1)(0x^0 + 1x^1)$ and get
$0x^0 + 0x^1 + 1x^2$ in the old notation. Thus the polynomial x^2 is really the
product of the polynomial x with itself. Similarly, the polynomial x^i is the
polynomial x times itself i times. Also, for each $a \in R$, a is a polynomial
belonging to $R[x]$. Hence it makes sense to multiply the polynomial a times
the polynomial x^i. The resulting polynomial is ax^i. (Check it in the original
notation!)

Now consider a polynomial

$$f(x) = a_0 * a_1 x * a_2 x^2 * \cdots * a_n x^n$$

in $R[x]$. For each i, we may consider the term $a_i x^i$ as a_i multiplied by x to
the power i. Moreover, the individual terms of $f(x)$ are each polynomials in
$R[x]$, and we know how to add polynomials. What is the result of adding

these individual terms as polynomials? The answer,

$$a_0 + a_1x + a_2x^2 + \cdots + a_nx^n,$$

is precisely the polynomial $f(x)$. Hence, where the symbol ∗ has appeared between terms of a polynomial, we may now put a plus sign. Thus every polynomial may be considered as a sum of one-term polynomials.

The ring $R[x]$ now consists of all polynomials

$$a_0 + a_1x + a_2x^2 + \cdots + a_nx^n,$$

where $a_0, a_1, \ldots, a_n \in R$ and n is a nonnegative integer. Furthermore, the terms a_ix^i mean a_i times x to the power i and the plus signs mean addition.

6.1.7 Definition. *Let $f(x)$ be a nonzero polynomial in x with coefficients in a commutative ring R with unity element. The **degree of $f(x)$**, denoted by **deg $f(x)$**, is the largest integer m such that the coefficient of x^m is not zero. If $f(x)$ has degree m and if a_m is the coefficient of x^m, then a_m is called the **leading coefficient** of $f(x)$. Terms which do not involve x—those which were written with x^0 before—are called **constant terms**.*

Observe that we have not defined degree for the zero polynomial. Hence, in order to discuss the degree of a polynomial, one must first know that the polynomial is nonzero. Polynomials which consist only of the constant term are usually called *constant polynomials*. By definition, the degree of all nonzero constant polynomials is zero. If $f(x) = 3x^2 + 4x^2 + 2x^5$, then $deg\, f(x) = 5$, the leading coefficient of $f(x)$ is 2, and the constant term of $f(x)$ is 0.

As we will now see, if R is an integral domain, "deg" is well behaved. However, if R is simply a commutative ring with unity element, it behaves rather badly.

6.1.8 Theorem. *Let R be an integral domain and let $f(x)$, $g(x)$ be nonzero elements of $R[x]$. Then*

$$deg\, (f(x)g(x)) = deg\, f(x) + deg\, g(x).$$

Proof. Suppose $deg\, f(x) = n$ and $deg\, g(x) = m$. Then

$$f(x) = a_0 + a_1 + \cdots + a_nx^n,$$

and

$$g(x) = b_0 + b_1x^1 + \cdots + b_mx^m$$

for some $a_0, a_1, \ldots, a_n, b_0, b_1, \ldots, b_m \in R$, where $a_n \neq 0$, $b_m \neq 0$. Since R is an integral domain, $a_nb_m \neq 0$. Hence, since a_nb_m is the coefficient of x^{n+m} in $f(x)g(x)$, we have

$$deg\, (f(x)g(x)) = n + m = deg\, f(x) + deg\, g(x).$$

We now have the following corollary to Theorem 6.1.8.

6.1.9 Corollary. *If R is an integral domain, then R[x] is an integral domain.*

Proof. Assume that R is an integral domain. Let $f(x)$, $g(x)$ be nonzero elements of $R[x]$. Then $f(x)$ and $g(x)$ both have a degree, and

$$deg\, f(x) + deg\, g(x) = deg\, (f(x)g(x)).$$

Hence $f(x)g(x)$ has a degree; this means that $f(x)g(x)$ is nonzero. Hence $R[x]$ has no zero divisors. That $R[x]$ is an integral domain now follows by Theorem 6.1.5.

6.1.10 Exercises

1. Prove the distributive laws for $R[x]$. Prove that $1x^0$ is the unity element.
2. Consider the following subsets of $R[x]$. Which are subrings of $R[x]$? Which are ideals of $R[x]$?
   a) All polynomials with zero constant term
   b) All polynomials of degree less than 11
   c) All polynomials with zero coefficients for all terms involving an *odd* power of x
   d) All polynomials with zero coefficients for all terms involving an *even* power of x
   e) All polynomials whose coefficients are multiples of 7
3. Let R, S be given commutative rings with unity element, and let $\alpha: R \to S$ be an epimorphism. Define a mapping $\alpha^*: R[x] \to S[x]$ by the following: If $f(x) = a_n x^n + \cdots + a_1 x + a_0 \in R[x]$, then

$$\alpha^*(f(x)) = \alpha(a_n)x^n + \cdots + \alpha(a_1)x + \alpha(a_0).$$

   Prove that α^* is an epimorphism.
4. Give an example to show that "*deg*" is ill behaved if R is not an integral domain; i.e., show that Theorem 6.1.8 is false if R is not an integral domain.
5. Let α be a mapping from $R[x]$ to $R[x]$ defined by $\alpha(f(x)) = f'(x)$ where ′ denotes differentiation. What properties does the mapping α have?

6.2 DIVISIBILITY AND THE DIVISION ALGORITHM

For the remainder of this chapter we will be interested in polynomials over an *arbitrary field F*. Then $F[x]$ is an integral domain. We want to consider results for $F[x]$ which are similar to those considered in Chapter 4 for the integral domain I of all integers. We extend the definition of divisors and develop a division algorithm. Then we proceed to prove a unique factorization theorem, just as we did in Chapter 4. In fact, with one small alteration, the proof of many theorems concerning $F[x]$ are the same as the proof of corresponding theorems for I. In Chapter 4 we made extensive use of the ordering on I. The small alteration necessary is that $F[x]$ may not be ordered. But each nonzero element of $F[x]$ has associated with it an integer—namely, its degree. We must rely on this fact where for results in I we used the ordering on I.

6.2.1 Definition. *Let $f(x)$, $g(x) \in F[x]$. Then $f(x)$ **divides** $g(x)$ if there exists $h(x) \in F[x]$ such that $f(x)h(x) = g(x)$. We denote this by $f(x) \mid g(x)$ and we also say $f(x)$ is a **factor** of $g(x)$, $f(x)$ is a **divisor** of $g(x)$, or $g(x)$ is a **multiple** of $f(x)$.*

The symbol $\nmid$ is used to denote "does not divide."

The nonzero elements of F divide every element of $F[x]$; for, if $c \in F$, $c \neq 0$; then for any $f(x) \in F[x]$, $c^{-1}f(x) \in F[x]$ and $c \cdot c^{-1}f(x) = f(x)$. Also, if $f(x) \mid g(x)$, then $cf(x) \mid g(x)$ for all nonzero $c \in F$. Consequently, there is no loss in generality when determining the divisors of a polynomial $f(x)$ if one assumes that the leading coefficient of $f(x)$ is 1. A polynomial whose leading coefficient is 1 is said to be *monic*.

Just as in the integers, there are certain polynomials which are important because of their divisibility properties.

6.2.2 Definition. *A polynomial $p(x) \in F[x]$ is an **irreducible** (or **prime**) polynomial over F if $p(x)$ has positive degree and $p(x)$ cannot be expressed as a product of polynomials of positive degree over F.*

Since the nonzero elements of F have degree zero, they cannot be irreducible polynomials. On the other hand, all polynomials of degree one over F are irreducible over F since the degree of the product of two polynomials of positive degree over F is greater than one.

Observe that the term defined in Definition 6.2.2 is "irreducible polynomial over F." The irreducibility or reducibility of a certain polynomial depends on the field involved. The factor polynomials used to determine whether a polynomial $f(x) \in F[x]$ is irreducible or not must also belong to $F[x]$. For instance, $x^2 - 2$ is irreducible over the field Q of rational numbers; however, if R is the field of real numbers, then in $R[x]$,

$$x^2 - 2 = (x - \sqrt{2})(x + \sqrt{2})$$

so that $x^2 - 2$ is reducible over R.

Irreducible polynomials over a field F play the same role for $F[x]$ as the primes do for the integers. After developing a division algorithm, we will prove that every polynomial in $F[x]$ can be written uniquely as a product of irreducible polynomials over F. The division algorithm (Theorem 4.1.3) which we developed for the integers played an important role in the theory of numbers in Chapter 4. We now develop a division algorithm for $F[x]$.

6.2.3 Theorem (Division Algorithm). *Let $f(x)$, $g(x)$ be polynomials over F with $g(x) \neq 0$. Then there exist unique polynomials $q(x)$ and $r(x)$ such that $f(x) = q(x)g(x) + r(x)$, and either $r(x) = 0$ or else $\deg r(x) < \deg g(x)$.*

Proof. We will prove the existence part of the theorem and leave the uniqueness part as an exercise. First let us consider two trivial cases. If $f(x) = 0$ or if $\deg f(x) < \deg g(x)$, we simply take $q(x) = 0$ and $r(x) = f(x)$. If $\deg g(x) = 0$, say $g(x) = a$ for some nonzero $a \in F$, then take $q(x) = a^{-1}f(x)$ and $r(x) = 0$. Hence we can assume that $f(x) \neq 0$ and $1 \leq \deg g(x) \leq \deg f(x)$.

We prove the result by induction on $n = \deg f(x)$. However, we will use the Strong Principle of Mathematical Induction; see 1.7.3, Exercise 3. Let S_n be the statement "If $f(x)$, $g(x) \in F[x]$ and $\deg f(x) = n$, then there exist polynomials $q(x)$, $r(x)$ in $F[x]$ such that $f(x) = q(x)g(x) + r(x)$, and either $r(x) = 0$ or $\deg r(x) < \deg g(x)$." If $n = 1$, then $1 = \deg f(x) = \deg g(x)$, and so $f(x) = ax + b$, $g(x) = cx + d$ where a, b, c, $d \in F$ and $a \neq 0$, $c \neq 0$. Then take $q(x) = ac^{-1}$ and $r(x) = b - ac^{-1}d$. Then S_1 is true.

Now assume that S_i is true for all positive integers $i < n$, and let $f(x)$, $g(x) \in F[x]$ with $\deg f(x) = n$. Then $f(x) = ax^n + \cdots$ for some nonzero $a \in F$. Then $g(x) = bx^m + \cdots$ for $1 \leq m \leq n$ and some nonzero $b \in F$. Now carry out one step in the usual "long division process" of dividing $f(x)$ by $g(x)$. Then

$$f(x) = ab^{-1}x^{n-m}g(x) + [f(x) - ab^{-1}x^{n-m}g(x)].$$

Set $h(x) = f(x) - ab^{-1}x^{n-m}g(x)$. Then the coefficient of x^n in $h(x)$ is zero; therefore $\deg h(x) < n$. Hence, by the induction hypothesis, there exist polynomials $q_1(x)$, $r(x) \in F[x]$ such that

$$h(x) = q_1(x)g(x) + r(x),$$

and

$$\text{either} \quad r(x) = 0 \quad \text{or} \quad \deg r(x) < \deg g(x).$$

Therefore

$$f(x) = [ab^{-1}x^{n-m} + q_1(x)]g(x) + r(x),$$

so by taking $q(x) = ab^{-1}x^{n-m} + q_1(x)$, we have proved that S_n is true. Thus, by the Strong Principle of Mathematical Induction, the theorem is proved.

As is the case for the integers, the $q(x)$ and $r(x)$ that satisfy the conclusion of the theorem are called the *quotient* and *remainder* respectively. Having established the division algorithm, we are in a position to obtain some rather useful results.

6.2.4 Definition. *Let $f(x) = a_nx^n + a_{n-1}x^{n-1} + \cdots + a_1x + a_0$ be a polynomial over F. For $c \in F$, $f(c)$ will be the element*

$$f(c) = a_nc^n + a_{n-1}c^{n-1} + \cdots + a_1c + a_0.$$

*Furthermore, if $f(c) = 0$, then c is said to be a **root** of the polynomial $f(x)$ over F.*

In a study of polynomials, one is often interested in determining the roots of a given polynomial. Every element of F is a root of the zero polynomial. The elements of $F[x]$ of degree 0 have no roots. Here again one must keep in mind the field involved. For instance, $x^2 - 2$ has two roots when considered as a polynomial over the field of real numbers, but it has none when considered as a polynomial over the field of rational numbers.

Let $f(x)$ be a polynomial over F, and let $c \in F$. If we divide $f(x)$ by $x - c$, the division algorithm guarantees the existence of polynomials $q(x)$ and $r(x)$ in $F[x]$ such that $f(x) = (x - c)q(x) + r(x)$, and either $r(x) = 0$ or $deg\, r(x) < deg\, (x - c)$. Hence either $r(x) = 0$ or $deg\, r(x) = 0$. In either case, $r(x)$ is an element of F; call it r. Then $f(c) = q(c)(c - c) + r$. Hence

$$f(x) = q(x)(x - c) + f(c).$$

Hence we immediately obtain the following corollaries to Theorem 6.2.3.

6.2.5 Corollary (Remainder Theorem). *If $f(x) \in F[x]$ and $c \in F$, then the remainder in the division of $f(x)$ by $x - c$ is $f(c)$.*

6.2.6 Corollary (Factor Theorem). *If $f(x) \in F[x]$ and $c \in F$, $(x - c) \,|\, f(x)$ if and only if $f(c) = 0$.*

Corollary 6.2.6 says that $(x - c) \,|\, f(x)$ if and only if c is a root of $f(x)$. This corollary is useful in proving the next theorem.

6.2.7 Theorem. *If $f(x)$ is a polynomial of positive degree n over F and if $c_1, c_2, \ldots, c_n$ are elements of F which are roots of $f(x)$, then*

$$f(x) = a(x - c_1)(x - c_2) \cdots (x - c_n)$$

where a is some element of F.

Proof. Let $n = deg\, f(x)$, and let S_n be the statement of the theorem. If $n = 1$, then $f(x) = ax + b$ for $a, b \in F, a \neq 0$. Moreover, since c_1 is a root, $f(c_1) = ac_1 + b = 0$. Hence $c_1 = -a^{-1}b$. Thus $f(x) = a(x - c_1)$, so S_1 is true. Assume that S_k is true. Let $f(x)$ be a polynomial of degree $k + 1$ over F with roots $c_1, \ldots, c_{k+1}$. Since c_{k+1} is a root of $f(x)$, the Factor Theorem implies that $f(x) = (x - c_{k+1})q(x)$ for some $q(x) \in F[x]$. Then $deg\, q(x) = k$ and $c_1, \ldots, c_k$ are roots of $q(x)$. Hence, by our induction assumption S_k,

$$q(x) = a(x - c_1) \cdots (x - c_k).$$

Thus

$$f(x) = a(x - c_1) \cdots (x - c_k)(x - c_{k+1}),$$

so S_{k+1} is true. Therefore, by the Principle of Mathematical Induction, the theorem is proved.

This theorem allows us to prove a theorem which we have all used quite often in elementary algebra courses.

6.2.8 Corollary. *A polynomial of degree n over F may have at most n distinct roots.*

Proof. Let $f(x)$ be a polynomial of degree n over F. Suppose $f(x)$ has $n + 1$ distinct roots; say $c_1, c_2, \ldots, c_{n+1}$. Since $c_1, \ldots, c_n$ are roots of $f(x)$,

$$f(x) = a(x - c_1) \cdots (x - c_n).$$

But $f(c_{n+1}) = 0$; so

$$a(c_{n+1} - c_1) \cdots (c_{n+1} - c_n) = 0.$$

Since F is an integral domain and $a \neq 0$, $c_{n+1} = c_i$ for some $i = 1, \ldots, n$. This contradicts the distinctness of $c_1, c_2, \ldots, c_{n+1}$. Hence $f(x)$ can have at most n roots.

One question which one must quite often attempt to answer in regard to a polynomial $f(x)$ over F is: "Is it irreducible?" In general, this is a very difficult question. However, the next theorem simplifies the problem for polynomials of degree two or three over F.

6.2.9 Theorem. *Let $f(x)$ be a polynomial of degree two or three over F. Then $f(x)$ is irreducible over F if and only if $f(x)$ has no roots over F.*

The proof is a simple application of Theorem 6.1.8 and is left as an exercise. It is important to observe that the result is false if $\deg f(x) \geq 4$. For instance, if F is the field of rational numbers, then the polynomial $(x^2 - 2)^2$ has no roots in F and clearly is not irreducible.

6.2.10 Exercises

1. Determine whether or not each of the following polynomials is irreducible over each of the given fields. The fields of rational numbers, real numbers, and complex numbers will be denoted by Q, R, and C respectively.

   a) $x^2 + x + 2$ over Q, R, and C
   b) $x^2 + 2x - 1$ over Q, R, and C
   c) $x^3 - 2$ over Q, R, and C
   d) $x^3 + 2$ over Q, R, and C
   e) $x^3 + 2x + 1$ over $I/(2)$, $I/(3)$, and $I/(7)$
   f) $x^2 + x + 2$ over $I/(3)$, $I/(5)$, and $I/(11)$
   g) $x^4 - 1$ over $I/(7)$ and $I/(19)$
   h) $x^4 + 1$ over $I/(2)$ and $I/(3)$

2. List all irreducible polynomials of degree less than or equal to five over the field $I/(2)$. (There are ten of them.)

3. Find all roots of each of the following polynomials over the given fields.
    a) $x^3 + 2x^2 + 3$ over $I/(3)$, $I/(5)$, and $I/(7)$
    b) $x^5 - x$ over $I/(3)$, $I/(5)$, and $I/(7)$
    c) $x^4 + 2x^2 + 1$ over Q, R, and C
    d) $x^4 + 6x^3 + 3x^2 + 6x + 2$ over $I/(7)$ and $I/(11)$

4. Prove the "uniqueness" part of Theorem 6.2.3.

5. Prove that a polynomial $f(x)$ over F has a factor of degree one in $F[x]$ if and only if $f(x)$ has a root in F.

6. Let $f(x)$, $g(x) \in F[x]$ where F is a field such that the number of elements in F is greater than the degrees of either $f(x)$ or $g(x)$. Suppose that $f(c) = g(c)$ for all $c \in F$. Prove that the two polynomials $f(x)$ and $g(x)$ are equal. (Hint: Consider the polynomial $h(x) = f(x) - g(x)$.)

7. In the remarks after Definition 6.2.1, we stated that there is no loss of generality in discussing the divisors of a polynomial if one assumes that it is monic. Prove this fact in detail.

6.3 GREATEST COMMON DIVISOR AND UNIQUE FACTORIZATION

In Chapter 4 we proved the existence of the greatest common divisor of two given nonzero integers using only the fact that the set of positive integers is well ordered and the division algorithm for the integers. We also proved that every nonzero integer can be expressed uniquely as a product of primes. The proof of this is based on a theorem and its corollary whose proofs use only the existence of the greatest common divisor of two given nonzero integers and the fact that the greatest common divisor can be expressed as a linear combination of the two integers.

In the last section, we developed a division algorithm for $F[x]$. Hence we can repeat the processes discussed above to obtain similar results for $F[x]$. The proofs are so nearly like those given in Chapter 4 for the corresponding results for I that they are omitted here and left to the reader.

6.3.1 Definition. *Let $f(x)$, $g(x)$ be given nonzero polynomials over F. The **greatest common divisor** (**g.c.d.**) of $f(x)$ and $g(x)$ is the monic polynomial $d(x) \in F[x]$ such that*

1) $d(x) \mid f(x)$, $d(x) \mid g(x)$, *and*

2) *if there exists $e(x) \in F[x]$ such that $e(x) \mid f(x)$ and $e(x) \mid g(x)$, then $e(x) \mid d(x)$.*

Since $d(x) \mid f(x)$ implies that $cd(x) \mid f(x)$ for all nonzero $c \in F$, we must require that the g.c.d. of $f(x)$ and $g(x)$ be *monic* in order to obtain a *unique* g.c.d. As in I, we say an expression of the form

$$f(x)m(x) + g(x)n(x)$$

where $m(x)$, $n(x) \in F[x]$ is a *linear combination of $f(x)$ and $g(x)$*. The proof of the following theorem is analogous to the proof of Theorem 4.2.2.

6.3.2 Theorem. *Let $f(x)$, $g(x)$ be given nonzero polynomials over F. Then the greatest common divisor $d(x)$ of $f(x)$ and $g(x)$ exists; and, in fact, there exist polynomials $m(x)$, $n(x) \in F[x]$ such that*

$$d(x) = f(x)m(x) + g(x)n(x).$$

Furthermore, $d(x)$ is the monic polynomial of least degree expressible as a linear combination of $f(x)$ and $g(x)$.

To determine the greatest common divisor of two integers, one usually uses the Euclidean Algorithm (4.2.6). The development of the Euclidean Algorithm depends only on a repeated use of the division algorithm. Hence we may carry out the same procedure for $F[x]$.

Let $f(x)$, $g(x)$ be given nonzero polynomials over F. By repeated application of Theorem 6.2.3, we obtain the following:

$$
\begin{aligned}
f(x) &= q_1(x)g(x) + r_1(x) &&\text{and} && \deg r_1(x) < \deg g(x), \\
g(x) &= q_2(x)r_1(x) + r_2(x) &&\text{and} && \deg r_2(x) < \deg r_1(x), \\
r_1(x) &= q_3(x)r_2(x) + r_3(x) &&\text{and} && \deg r_3(x) < \deg r_2(x), \\
&\quad\vdots &&&&\quad\vdots \\
r_{k-2}(x) &= q_k(x)r_{k-1}(x) + r_k(x) &&\text{and} && \deg r_k(x) < \deg r_{k-1}(x). \\
r_{k-1}(x) &= q_{k+1}(x)r_k(x).
\end{aligned}
$$

Assume that $r_k(x)$ is the last nonzero remainder. If $r_k(x)$ has leading coefficient a, then $a^{-1}r_k(x)$ is monic. Also, as in the case of the integers, $a^{-1}r_k(x)$ is the greatest common divisor of $f(x)$ and $g(x)$. Furthermore, using the above equations, one can express $a^{-1}r_k(x)$ as a linear combination of $f(x)$ and $g(x)$.

As a simple numerical example, let us compute the g.c.d. of $f(x) = x^4 + 4x^3 + 4x + 4$ and $g(x) = 4x^2 + 4x + 1$ over $I/(5)$.

$$
\begin{aligned}
x^4 + 4x^3 + 4x + 4 &= (4x^2 + 2x + 2)(4x^2 + 4x + 1) + 4x + 2, \\
4x^2 + 4x + 1 &= (x + 3)(4x + 2).
\end{aligned}
$$

Hence $4x + 2$ is the last nonzero remainder. Therefore $4(4x + 2) = x + 3$ is the g.c.d.

Next we state the analogs to Theorem 4.2.7 and Corollary 4.2.8.

6.3.3 Theorem. *If a polynomial $p(x)$ which is irreducible over F divides a product $f(x)g(x)$ of polynomials over F, then $p(x) \mid f(x)$ or $p(x) \mid g(x)$.*

6.3.4 Corollary. *If a polynomial $p(x)$ which is irreducible over F divides a product $f_1(x)f_2(x) \cdots f_n(x)$ of polynomials over F, then $p(x) \mid f_i(x)$ for some $i = 1, \ldots, n$.*

Using this corollary, one can develop the unique factorization theorem by paraphrasing the proof of Theorems 4.3.1 and 4.3.2. However, to obtain uniqueness we must require that the factors be monic.

6.3.5 Theorem. *Every polynomial $f(x)$ of positive degree over F with leading coefficient a can be expressed uniquely as a product of a times finitely many monic irreducible polynomials over F.*

6.3.6 Exercises

1. Write out a proof of Theorem 6.3.2.
2. Write out a proof of Theorem 6.3.3.
3. Write out a proof of Corollary 6.3.4.
4. Write out a proof of Theorem 6.3.5.
5. Determine the greatest common divisor of each pair of polynomials below over the indicated fields, and express it as a linear combination of the two polynomials.
   a) $2x^3 + x + 4$, $x^2 - 2x + 4$ over Q, $I/(5)$, and $I/(7)$.
   b) $2x^4 - 3$, $x^3 + 2x^2 + x + 1$ over Q, R, and $I/(5)$.
   c) $x^3 + x^2 + x + 1$, $x^2 + x + 1$ over Q, $I/(2)$, and $I/(3)$.
6. Write all polynomials given in 6.2.10, Exercise 1 as a product of monic irreducible polynomials over the fields indicated.

6.4 POLYNOMIALS OVER THE FIELD OF RATIONAL NUMBERS

Throughout this section we will be considering polynomials over the field Q of rational numbers. Theorems will be proved which will aid in determining the roots of polynomials over Q and in deciding which polynomials are irreducible over Q.

There is no loss of generality if, when proving a theorem about the roots of a polynomial over Q, one assumes that the polynomial has integral coefficients; for, let $f(x)$ be a polynomial of positive degree over Q. If a is the least common multiple of the denominators of the coefficients of $f(x)$, then $af(x)$ has integral coefficients. Furthermore, $af(x)$ and $f(x)$ have identically the same roots in Q.

6.4.1 Theorem. *Let $f(x) = a_n x^n + \cdots + a_1 x + a_0$ be a polynomial of positive degree n with integral coefficients. In order that a rational number r/s in reduced form be a root of $f(x)$, we must have $r \mid a_0$ and $s \mid a_n$.*

Proof. If r/s is a root of $f(x)$, then

$$a_n(r/s)^n + a_{n-1}(r/s)^{n-1} + \cdots + a_1(r/s) + a_0 = 0.$$

Now multiplying by s^n and subtracting $a_0 s^n$ gives

$$(a_n r^{n-1} + \cdots + a_1 s^{n-1})r = -a_0 s^n.$$

Since $(s, r) = 1$ and $r \mid a_0 s^n$, we must have $r \mid a_0$, by 4.2.11, Exercise 6. By a similar argument, $s \mid a_n$.

Consider, as an example of an application of this theorem, the polynomial $f(x) = 3x^3 + x^2 + -12x - 4$. The only possible roots of $f(x)$ in Q are fractions r/s where $r \mid 4$ and $s \mid 3$. Hence the only possible rational roots are $\pm 1, \pm 2, \pm 4, \pm 1/3, \pm 2/3$, and $\pm 4/3$. By checking these possibilities, one can readily determine the roots of $f(x)$ in Q: $-1/3, 2, -2$.

In general, it is difficult to determine whether or not a given polynomial is irreducible over a given field. Next we will prove Eisenstein's Criterion, which provides information concerning the irreducibility of polynomials over Q. First we need some preliminary results.

6.4.2 Definition. *A polynomial $f(x)$ with integer coefficients is said to be* **primitive** *if the greatest common divisor of its coefficients is* 1.

6.4.3 Theorem. *The product of primitive polynomials is primitive.*

Proof. Let $f(x)$, $g(x)$ be primitive polynomials. Suppose that $f(x)g(x)$ is not primitive. Then there exists a prime p which divides every coefficient of $f(x)g(x)$. Let α be the epimorphism from I onto $I/(p)$ defined by $\alpha(n) = [n]$ for all $n \in I$. Then, by 6.1.10, Exercise 3, α^* is an epimorphism from $I[x]$ onto $I/(p)[x]$. Moreover,

$$\alpha^*\big(f(x)\big) \cdot \alpha^*\big(g(x)\big) = \alpha^*\big(f(x)g(x)\big) = 0$$

since the image of every coefficient of $f(x)g(x)$ under α is 0. Since $I/(p)[x]$ is an integral domain, either $\alpha^*\big(f(x)\big) = 0$ or $\alpha^*\big(g(x)\big) = 0$. Hence p divides all the coefficients of $f(x)$ or of $g(x)$. Thus $f(x)$ or $g(x)$ is not primitive, a contradiction which establishes the theorem.

The next theorem is due to Carl Friedrich Gauss (1777–1855), a German mathematician who is often referred to as "The Prince of Mathematics." The theorem states that a polynomial with integral coefficients is irreducible over Q if and only if it cannot be factored into a product of two polynomials of positive degree with integral coefficients.

6.4.4 Theorem (Gauss' lemma). *Let $f(x)$ be a polynomial of positive degree with integral coefficients such that $f(x) = g(x)h(x)$, where $g(x)$, $h(x) \in Q[x]$. Then there exist polynomials $g_1(x)$, $h_1(x) \in I[x]$ such that $f(x) = g_1(x)h_1(x)$.*

Proof. Without loss of generality, we may assume that $f(x)$ is primitive. By clearing denominators and factoring out common factors, we can write $f(x) = (a/b)g_1(x)h_1(x)$, where $a, b \in I$ and both $g_1(x)$ and $h_1(x)$ have integral coefficients and are primitive. Hence $g_1(x)h_1(x)$ is primitive. Writing $bf(x) = ag_1(x)h_1(x)$, one sees that the greatest common divisor of the coefficients of the left-hand side is b, whereas the greatest common divisor of the coefficients on the right-hand is a. Thus $a = b$ so that $f(x) = g_1(x)h_1(x)$.

The next theorem is due to a German mathematician F. M. G. Eisenstein (1823–1852).

6.4.5 Theorem (Eisenstein's Criterion). *Let*

$$f(x) = a_n x^n + \cdots + a_1 x + a_0$$

be a polynomial of positive degree with integral coefficients. If there exists a prime integer p such that

1) $p \mid a_i$ *for* $i = 0, 1, \ldots, n - 1$,
2) $p \nmid a_n$, *and*
3) $p^2 \nmid a_0$,

then $f(x)$ is irreducible over Q.

Proof. Without loss of generality, we may assume that $f(x)$ is primitive since factoring out the greatest common divisor of the coefficients of $f(x)$ does not change the hypothesis since $p \nmid a_n$. Suppose $f(x)$ factors into polynomials of positive degree over Q. Then by Gauss' Lemma, $f(x)$ factors into a product of polynomials of positive degree with integral coefficients; say

$$f(x) = (b_s x^s + \cdots + b_1 x + b_0)(c_t x^t + \cdots + c_1 x + c_0)$$

where the b's and c's are integers and $r > 0$, $s > 0$. Then $a_0 = b_0 c_0$. Since $p \mid a_0$ and $p^2 \nmid a_0$, by Theorem 4.2.7, $p \mid b_0$ or $p \mid c_0$, but not both. Suppose $p \mid b_0$ and $p \nmid c_0$. Not all the coefficients $b_s, \ldots, b_1, b_0$ are divisible by P since not all the coefficients of $f(x)$ are divisible by p. Let b_r be the last b not divisible by p; i.e., let b_r be the coefficient such that $p \nmid b_r$ and $p \mid b_i$ for $0 \le i < r$. Consider the coefficient a_r:

$$a_r = b_r c_0 + b_{r-1} c_1 + \cdots + b_1 c_{r-1} + b_0 c_r.$$

Since $p \mid a_r$ and $p \mid b_i$ for $0 \le i < r$, p must also divide $b_r c_0$. But this is impossible, since $p \nmid b_r$ and $p \nmid c_0$. Hence $f(x)$ is irreducible. ∎

6.4.6 Exercises

1. Complete the proof of Theorem 6.4.1 by proving that $s \mid a_n$.
2. Find all the roots in Q of the following polynomials.
   a) $x^4 + x^3 - 9x^2 + 11x - 4$ b) $9x^4 + 6x^3 + 19x^2 + 12x + 2$
   c) $4x^5 + x^3 + x^2 - 3x + 1$ d) $4x^3 + 3x^2 + 6x + 12$
   e) $x^5 + x^4 + x^3 + x^2 + x + 1$ f) $x^{121} - x^{64} + 2x^{17} - 1$
   g) $x^9 + 2x^8 - 2$.

3. Prove that the polynomial $x^n - p$ is irreducible over Q for any integer n and any prime p.

_.5 THE RING OF POLYNOMIALS MODULO $f(x)$

There is still one more important concept which we developed for the integers and which can be copied in $F[x]$. We have shown that the ring $I/(n)$ of integers modulo n is a commutative ring with unity element, and if, in addition, n is a prime, $I/(n)$ is a field. The outline of our development and the proofs of the theorems for I can readily be adapted to $F[x]$. However, "irreducible polynomial" is used to replace "prime integer."

Let $f(x)$ be a given polynomial of positive degree over F. Define a relation $\sim$ on $F[x]$ by setting "$g(x) \sim h(x)$ if and only if $g(x) - h(x)$ is a multiple of $f(x)$" for all $g(x), h(x) \in F[x]$.

6.5.1 Theorem. *The relation $\sim$ is an equivalence relation on $F[x]$.*

The proof is straightforward and is left as an exercise.

Let $[f(x)]$ denote the equivalence class of $f(x)$. Let $F[x]/(f(x))$ denote the set of all equivalence classes. For $[g(x)], [h(x)] \in F[x]/(f(x))$ define

$$[g(x)] + [h(x)] = [g(x) + h(x)]$$

and

$$[g(x)] \cdot [h(x)] = [g(x)h(x)].$$

6.5.2 Theorem. *The addition and multiplication given above are well-defined binary operations on $F[x]/(f(x))$ which make $F[x]/(f(x))$ into a commutative ring with unity element.*

The proof is similar to the proof of Example 2 in Section 3.3 and hence is omitted.

6.5.3 Theorem. *Then $F[x]/(f(x))$ is a field if and only if $f(x)$ is irreducible over F.*

This proof is also omitted. Compare this theorem to Theorem 5.2.3.

Let $f(x)$ be a polynomial of positive degree over F and irreducible over F. Let $a, b \in F$. If $[a] = [b]$, then $a \sim b$ so that $a - b$ is a multiple of $f(x)$. But this can happen only if $a = b$. Consequently, the mapping from F to $F[x]/(f(x))$ which takes $a \in F$ onto $[a] \in F[x]/(f(x))$ is a monomorphism. Thus, as usual, we will identify the elements of F with their image in $F[x]/(f(x))$. Hence F is considered as a subfield of $F[x]/(f(x))$, and we write "a" instead of "$[a]$" for elements of $F[x]/(f(x))$.

To determine the equivalence classes, one looks at the differences of two polynomials and picks out the differences which are a multiple of $f(x)$. Since any multiple of $f(x)$ is also a multiple of $a^{-1}f(x)$ where a is the leading coefficient of $f(x)$, we may assume that $f(x)$ is monic. Let us write

$$f(x) = x^n + a_{n-1}x^{n-1} + \cdots + a_1 x + a_0,$$

where $a_{n-1}, \ldots, a_1, a_0 \in F$. The elements of $F[x]/(f(x))$ are equivalence classes of the form $[g(x)]$ where $g(x) \in F[x]$. But by the division algorithm

(6.2.3), for any $g(x) \in F[x]$, there exist unique polynomials $q(x)$, $r(x) \in F[x]$
such that

$$g(x) = q(x)f(x) + r(x) \quad \text{and} \quad r(x) = 0 \quad \text{or} \quad deg\, r(x) < n.$$

Thus $[g(x)] = [r(x)]$ where $r(x) = 0$ or $deg\, r(x) < n$. Hence the nonzero
elements of $F[x]/(f(x))$ are precisely the equivalence classes of those polynomials of degree less than n; hence an arbitrary element of $F[x]/(f(x))$ can
be expressed by

$$[b_{n-1}x^{n-1} + \cdots + b_1x + b_0]$$

where $b_{n-1}, \ldots, b_1, b_0 \in F$. If we apply the definitions of multiplication
and addition to this, we obtain

$$[b_{n-1}][x^{n-1}] + \cdots + [b_1][x] + [b_0].$$

We have agreed previously to replace elements of the form $[b]$ where $b \in F$
by b itself. Also note that $[x][x] = [x^2]$ and, in general, $[x^m] = [x]^m$ for all
positive integers m. If we substitute the symbol j for $[x]$, an arbitrary element
of $F[x]/(f(x))$ can be written as

$$b_{n-1}j^{n-1} + \cdots + b_1j + b_0$$

where $b_{n-1}, \ldots, b_1, b_0 \in F$.

Clearly, if we add two elements of this form, we get another element of this
form. What about multiplication? Recall that $[f(x)] = 0$ in $F[x]/(f(x))$.
Hence $j^n + a_{n-1}j^{n-1} + \cdots + a_0 = 0$. Thus

(1) $$j^n = -a_{n-1}j^{n-1} - \cdots - a_1j - a_0$$

and furthermore,

$$
\begin{aligned}
(2) \quad j^{n+1} &= -a_{n-1}j^n - \cdots - a_1j^2 - a_0j \\
&= (a_{n-1}^2 - a_{n-2})j^{n-1} + (a_{n-1}a_{n-2} - a_{n-3})j^{n-2} + \cdots \\
&\quad + (a_{n-1}a_1 - a_0)j + a_{n-1}a_0
\end{aligned}
$$

by substituting (1) for j^n in (2). In a similar manner, for all positive integers
k, j^{n+k} can be written in the form $c_{n-1}j^{n-1} + \cdots + c_1j + c_0$, where
$c_{n-1}, \ldots, c_1, c_0 \in F$.

Let us consider a specific example: Let F be the field of rational numbers,
and let $f(x) = x^2 - 2$. Then $f(x)$ is irreducible over F. The elements of
$F[x]/(x^2 - 2)$ are expressions of the form.

$$aj + b$$

where a, b are rational numbers. Moreover, $j^2 = 2$. Hence, for

$$aj + b, \, cj + d \in F[x]/(x^2 - 2),$$

we have

$$(aj + b)(cj + d) = (ad + bc)j + (bd + 2ac).$$

Next we have a theorem which is extremely important in the study of fields. We have seen that, given a polynomial $f(x)$ over a field F, $f(x)$ may or may not have any roots in F. The next theorem states that there always exists a field E which contains F such that $f(x)$ has a root in E.

6.5.4 Theorem. *Given a polynomial $f(x)$ of positive degree over F, there exists a field E which contains F such that $f(x)$ has a root in E.*

Proof. The polynomial $f(x)$ can be written as a product of polynomials over F which are irreducible over F. Let $p(x)$ be one of these factors. Then $E = F[x]/\big(p(x)\big)$ is a field, and by our identification, E contains F. Moreover, continuing to denote $[x]$ by j, $p(j) = 0$. Hence j is a root of $p(x)$, and hence of $f(x)$, in E.

6.5.5 Exercises

1. Prove that $\sim$ is an equivalence relation on $F[x]$.
2. Prove that the addition and multiplication defined on $F[x]/\big(f(x)\big)$ are well defined.
3. Prove Theorem 6.5.2.
4. Prove Theorem 6.5.3.
5. Let R be the field of real numbers. Prove that $R[x]/(x^2 + 1)$ is a field which is isomorphic to the field of complex numbers.
6. Prove that $x^2 + x + 4$ is irreducible over $F = I/(11)$ and that

$$F[x]/(x^2 + x + 4)$$

   is a field having 121 elements.
7. Construct a field having 49 elements; 343 elements; p^n-elements where p is a prime and n is any integer.

ADDITIONAL REFERENCES FOR CHAPTER 6

BARNES, WILFRED E., *Introduction to Abstract Algebra*, Boston: Heath and Company (1963).

HERSTEIN, I. N., *Topics in Algebra*, New York: Blaisdell (1964).

McCOY, NEAL H., *Introduction to Modern Algebra*, Boston: Allyn and Bacon (1960).

WHITESITT, J. ELDON, *Principles of Modern Algebra*, Reading, Massachusetts: Addison-Wesley (1964).

CHAPTER 7

THE REAL NUMBER SYSTEM

The world in which we live is governed by the system of real numbers. We accept the real numbers and their properties simply because we have been told that they exist and that the properties are true. However, it is important that we prove through logical inference that the system of real numbers exists and that the properties of the real numbers which we have assumed to be true are actually true.

The construction of the real numbers involves a series of constructions, each of which is important in itself. First one obtains the set N of natural numbers, then the set I of integers. We have seen in Section 5.3 that the set Q of rational numbers can be obtained from I. Finally, the system of real numbers is obtained from Q.

In the development of the real numbers presented here, we will take the attitude that the reader is capable of counting and hence is familiar with the set $N = \{1, 2, 3, \ldots\}$ of natural numbers. However, we will indicate without extensive proofs how one obtains N from a system of axioms. We will define multiplication, addition, and an ordering and will list some of the properties of N. The development of the set I of integers follows rather easily from N and will be sketched in the sequel. Addition, multiplication, and an ordering will be defined on I, but the proof that they make I into an ordered integral domain will be left primarily to the reader. From this point, we have seen that Q is an ordered field. This construction and proof are not repeated. More care will be given to the development of the set R of real numbers. Definitions will be carefully stated, and we will prove in some detail that R is an ordered field which has the additional property of being *complete*. In conclusion, a short section is included which outlines the development of the field C of complex numbers from R.

7.1 THE NATURAL NUMBERS

We want to construct the system of natural numbers, assuming as little as possible. We will start with a system of axioms and, by making the proper definitions, we will obtain a system of numbers which we call the system of *natural numbers* $\{1, 2, \ldots\}$. One standard set of axioms which is used as a basis of the system of natural numbers is called *Peano's Postulates* since they are attributed to the Italian mathematician Giuseppe Peano (1858–1932). We assume that there exists a set N, called the *natural numbers*, which satisfies the following axioms.

7.1.1 Peano's Postulates.

1) $1 \in N$.
2) *There exists a one-to-one mapping from N onto the set of elements of N different from 1. The image of $n \in N$ is denoted by n^* and is called the **successor** of n.*
3) *For any set $M \subseteq N$ such that $1 \in M$ and $n \in M$ implies $n^* \in M$, $M = N$. (This is known as the **induction** axiom.)*

Intuitively, n^* may be thought of as $n + 1$; in fact, we can define n^* to be $n + 1$. To define addition so that the associative law holds, we must at least have $n + (m + 1) = (n + m) + 1$ for all $m, n \in N$; i.e., we must have $n + m^* = (n + m)^*$. It can be shown that there is exactly *one* binary operation $+$ on N such that $n^* = n + 1$ for all $n \in N$ and such that $n + m^* = (n + m)^*$ for all $m, n \in N$. Hence we make the following definition.

7.1.2 Definition. *The operation $+$ is the unique binary operation on N such that $n^* = n + 1$ and $n + m^* = (n + m)^*$ for all $m, n \in N$.*

What about multiplication? Surely we wish to have $n \cdot 1 = n$ for all $n \in N$. Moreover, if the distributive law is to hold for N, we must have

$$n \cdot (m + 1) = (n \cdot m) + (n \cdot 1);$$

that is we must have $n \cdot m^* = (n \cdot m) + n$. It can be shown that there is exactly *one* binary operation $\cdot$ which satisfies these condtiions. Hence we use it for the multiplication on N.

7.1.3 Definition. *The operation $\cdot$ is the unique binary operation on N such that $n \cdot 1 = n$ and $n \cdot m^* = (n \cdot m) + n$ for all $m, n \in N$.*

The natural number $m \cdot n$ will often be written as mn.

7.1.4 Theorem. *Both $+$ and $\cdot$ are associative, commutative binary operations on N. Furthermore $\cdot$ is left- and right-distributive over $+$.*

The proof of the associativity and commutativity of addition will be given here; the remainder of the proof is left as an exercise.

Proof. Let $M = \{p \in N \mid (n + m) + p = n + (m + p) \text{ for all } m, n \in N\}$. We will use axiom (3) to prove that $M = N$, thus proving the associativity of $+$ on N. Now $1 \in M$ since

$$(n + m) + 1 = (n + m)^* = n + m^* = n + (m + 1).$$

Now assume that $p \in N$; i.e., assume that $(n + m) + p = n + (m + p)$. Then

$$(n + m) + (p + 1) = (n + m) + p^* = ((n + m) + p)^*$$
$$= (n + (m + p))^* = n + (m + p)^*$$
$$= n + (m + p^*) = n + (m + (p + 1)).$$

Hence $p + 1 \in M$. Axiom (3) then implies that $M = N$.

Now let

$$M = \{n \in N \mid m + n = n + m \text{ for all } m \in N\}.$$

Again we wish to show that $1 \in M$. However, to show that $1 \in M$ will require a separate induction argument based on Axiom (3). Having completed that, the proof of the commutativity of $+$ is similar to the above proof.

7.1.5 Definition. *If m, $n \in N$, then $m < n$ if there exists $p \in N$ such that $m + p = n$.*

We use $m < n$ and $n > m$ interchangeably. Also, $m \leq n$ means $m < n$ or $m = n$. This definition gives an *ordering* on N.

7.1.6 Theorem. *Let $m, n, p \in N$. Then the following hold.*

1) $<$ *is transitive, but not reflexive or symmetric.*

2) $n < n^*$ *and* $1 \leq n$.

3) *Exactly one of the following is true: $m = n$, $m < n$, $n < m$. (This is the trichotomy law.)*

4) $n < m$ *if and only if* $n + p < m + p$.

5) $n < m$ *if and only if* $np < mp$.

6) *If $p \leq m \leq p^*$, then $p = m$ or $p^* = m$.*

We leave the proof of this theorem as an exercise.

The system of natural numbers has an important property, of which we have made extensive use in this book. It is appropriate that we give a proof of it now. The property is that N is *well ordered*. First some definitions are needed.

7.1.7 Definition.

1) *Let $M \subseteq N$. Then $a \in M$ is a **least element** of M if $a \leq b$ for all $b \in M$.*

2) *A set X is **well ordered** if every nonempty subset of X has a least element.*

7.1.8 Theorem. *The set N of natural numbers is well ordered.*

Proof. Let M be a nonempty subset of N. We must show that M has a least element. Let

$$K = \{k \mid k \in N, k \leq m \text{ for all } m \in M\}.$$

Since M is nonempty, there exists $m \in M$. Then $m^* \notin K$ since $m^* > m$, by Theorem 7.1.6, (2). Hence $K \neq N$. But $1 \in K$ since $1 \leq n$ for all $n \in N$, also by Theorem 7.1.6, (2). Hence there exists $k \in K$ such $k^* \notin M$; for, if such a k did not exist, then $K = N$, which is not true. Since $k^* \notin M$, there must exist $m \in M$ such that $k^* > m$. But since $k \in K$, we must have $k \leq m$. Hence, from Theorem 7.1.6, (6), we see that $k = m$. Hence $k \in M$ and $k \leq m$ for all $m \in M$. Therefore k is the least element of M.

Thus we have the natural numbers and some of their properties. Henceforth, when we mention the *system N of natural numbers*, it will be understood that we mean the system consisting of N, $+$, $\cdot$, and $<$ as we have defined them above.

7.1.9 Exercises

1. a) Prove that $1 + n = n + 1$ for all $n \in N$.
   b) Use (a) to prove $n + m = m + n$ for all $m, n \in N$.
   c) Prove that $\cdot$ is left- and right-distributive over $+$.
   d) Prove that $\cdot$ is associative and commutative. (Hint: Use (c)).
   e) Prove that $n^* \neq n$ for each $n \in N$.
   f) Prove that $n \neq m + n$ for all $m, n \in N$.

2. Prove all parts of Theorem 7.1.6.

3. Prove that there is one and only one addition on N which satisfies $n^* = n + 1$ and $n + m^* = (n + m)^*$ for all $m, n \in N$.

4. Prove that there is one and only one multiplication on N which satisfies $n \cdot 1 = n$ and $n \cdot m^* = (n \cdot m) + n$ for all $m, n \in N$.

7.2 THE INTEGERS

Intuitively, the way one obtains the set I of integers from N is to consider the difference of two natural numbers. Each integer can be expressed as the difference of two natural numbers, and conversely, the difference of two natural numbers is an integer. However, this representation of the integers is not unique; for $-3 = 2 - 5 = 7 - 10$ and $4 = 9 - 5 = 114 - 110$. Hence we must consider a certain integer r to be represented by all pairs of natural numbers whose difference is r; hence we must consider the pairs (m_1, n_1) and (m_2, n_2) of natural numbers to be equal if $m_1 - n_1 = m_2 - n_2$. However, in truth we cannot subtract natural numbers. We avoid this apparent dilemma by saying (m_1, n_1) and (m_2, n_2) are equal if $m_1 + n_2 = m_2 + n_1$.

> **7.2.1 Definition.** Let $J = \{(m, n) \mid m, n \in N\}$. *Define* $\sim$ *on* J *by*
>
> $$(m_1, n_1) \sim (m_2, n_2) \qquad \text{if and only if} \qquad m_1 + n_2 = m_2 + n_1$$
>
> *for all* $(m_1, n_1), (m_2, n_2) \in J$.
>
> That is, $\sim$ is a relation on J.

7.2.2 Theorem. *The relation* $\sim$ *is an equivalence relation on J.*

The proof is left as an exercise.

7.2.3 Definition. *Denote the equivalence class of* $(m, n) \in J$ *by* $[m, n]$. *Let I be the set of all equivalence classes; that is,* $I = \{[m, n] \mid m, n \in N\}$; *then I is called the set of integers. Let* $[m_1, n_1]$ *and* $[m_2, n_2]$ *be elements of I. Define* $+$ *and* $\cdot$ *by*

$$[m_1, n_1] + [m_2, n_2] = [m_1 + m_2, n_1 + n_2]$$

and

$$[m_1, n_1] \cdot [m_2, n_2] = [m_1 m_2 + n_1 n_2, m_1 n_2 + m_2 n_1].$$

7.2.4 Theorem. *The operations* $+$ *and* $\cdot$ *are well defined and make I into a commutative ring with unity element.*

Next we must define an ordering on I. If the integers $[m, n_1]$ and $[m_2, n_2]$ are considered to be the differences $m_1 - n_1$ and $m_2 - n_2$, it is intuitively clear that the correct definition of an ordering $<$ on I must be $[m_1, n_1] < [m_2, n_2]$ if $m_1 - n_1 < m_2 - n_2$. But again, since we cannot subtract natural numbers, we use the following definition.

7.2.5 Definition. *Define* $<$ *on I by* $[m_1, n_1] < [m_2, n_2]$ *if and only if* $m_1 + n_2 < m_2 + n_1$ *for all* $[m_1, n_1], [m_2, n_2] \in I.$

Even though we use the same symbols $+$, $\cdot$, and $<$ for the operations and ordering on both N and I, there should be no confusion. If the elements involved are natural numbers, then $+$, $\cdot$, and $<$ are those defined on N; on the other hand, when integers are involved, by $+$, $\cdot$, and $<$ we mean the operations and ordering we have just defined.

When we write $m_1 + n_2 < m_2 + n_1$ in Definition 7.2.5, the ordering $<$ is the ordering which we have previously defined on the natural numbers N. In Definition 7.2.5 we have defined $<$ on equivalence classes, and consequently, we must concern ourselves with the question of whether or not $<$ is well defined. Suppose that

$$[m_1, n_1] = [m'_1, n'_1] \qquad \text{and} \qquad [m_2, n_2] = [m'_2, n'_2].$$

Then it is a rather routine matter to prove that $m_1 + n_2 < m_2 + n_1$ if and only if $m'_1 + n'_2 < m'_2 + n'_1$. This proves that $<$ is indeed well defined. Next we list some of the properties of $<$ on I and leave the proof as an exercise. It should be no surprise that the proofs of the properties of the order relation $<$ on I depend heavily on the properties of $<$ on N.

7.2.6 Theorem. *The following properties hold for all* $a, b, c \in I.$

1) *Exactly one of the following is true:* $a = b$, $a < b$, *or* $a > b$. *(This is the trichotomy law for I.)*

2) $a < b$ *if and only if* $a + c < b + c$.

3) *Let a > 0. Then b > c if and only if ab < ac.*

4) *Let a < 0. Then b < c if and only if ab > ac.*

Again we leave the proof as an exercise.

Using parts (1), (3), and (4) of Theorem 7.2.6, one can easily show that the cancellation law of multiplication holds in I.   Hence, by Theorem 5.1.2, I is an integral domain.   In fact, if we define $a \in I$ to be *positive* if $a > 0$, then the set I_p of positive elements of I satisfy the conditions of Definition 5.4.1. Hence I is an ordered integral domain.

Furthermore, by 7.2.7, Exercise 5, there exists a one-to-one mapping from N onto I_p which preserves $+$, $\cdot$, and $<$. Hence we can consider N as a subset of I by identifying elements of N with their images under α.   Thus $N \subseteq I$.

In Section 5.3, we constructed the field of quotients of an integral domain. When the integral domain is I, the field of quotients is the field Q of rational numbers. Moreover, under an identification, I is considered as a subring of Q; hence we now have $N \subseteq I \subseteq Q$. In Section 5.5, using the ordering on I, we defined an ordering, also denoted by $<$, on Q and proved that Q is an ordered field.

7.2.7 Exercises

1. Prove Theorem 7.2.2.

2. a) Prove that $+$ is well defined on I.
   b) Prove that $\cdot$ is well defined on I.
   c) Prove that for $n, m \in N$, $[n, n] = [m, m]$ and that this is the zero element of I.
   d) Prove that for $n, m \in N$, $[n^*, n] = [m^*, m]$ and that this is the unity element of I.
   e) Complete the proof that I is a commutative ring.

3. Prove Theorem 7.2.6.

4. Prove in detail that I is an ordered integral domain with $I_p = \{x \in I \mid x > 0\}$ as the set of positive elements.

5. Find a one-to-one mapping α from N onto I_p such that

$$\alpha(m + n) = \alpha(m) + \alpha(n), \qquad \alpha(m \cdot n) = \alpha(m) \cdot \alpha(n)$$

for all $m, n \in N$ and such that for $m, n \in N$

$$\text{if} \quad m < n, \quad \text{then} \quad \alpha(m) < \alpha(n).$$

(The mapping α has the properties of a homomorphism, but I_p and N are not rings.)

7.3 THE REAL NUMBERS

It is a common practice to envision the numbers which we use as being the points on a line. However, from Theorem 5.5.4, we know that there is no rational number b such that $b^2 = 2$.   Hence the rational numbers do not "fill up" the number line, so there is a need for a larger, more comprehensive number system. This system is the system of real numbers.

We will construct the system S of positive real numbers; then the system of all real numbers is obtained from S, exactly as the integers are obtained from the natural numbers, by considering equivalence classes which represent the differences of two positive real numbers. There are two common methods for constructing the system of positive real numbers from the system of rational numbers. One is the *Cauchy-sequence* method, named for the French mathematician Augustin Cauchy (1789–1857). The other is the *Dedekind-cut* method. Although other men made contributions to this theory, it is usually attributed to the German mathematicians Georg Cantor (1845–1918) and Richard Dedekind (1831–1916).

A Dedekind cut is a special kind of subset of the set Q_p of positive rational numbers. These Dedekind cuts will correspond to the positive real numbers.

7.3.1 Definition. *A subset D of Q_p is a **Dedekind cut** if the following conditions hold.*

1) *$D \neq \emptyset$ and $D \neq Q_p$.*
2) *If $d \in D$ and a is an arbitrary element of Q_p such that $a < d$, then $a \in D$.*
3) *If $d \in D$, then there exists $c \in D$ such that $d < c$.*

Condition (2) states that if a Dedekind cut contains a positive rational number r, then it contains all positive rationals less than r. Condition (3) states that a Dedekind cut has no largest element. We will often shorten "Dedekind cut" to "cut."

As an example of a Dedekind cut, let $a \in Q_p$ and define

$$D_a = \{b \in Q_p \mid b < a\}.$$

Then it is a routine matter to verify that the three conditions of Definition 7.3.1 hold. Hence D_a is a cut for all $a \in Q_p$. This shows that to every positive rational number there corresponds a Dedekind cut.

Another example of a Dedekind cut is provided by setting

$$D = \{a \in Q_p \mid a^2 < 2.\}$$

Let us verify that D is in fact a Dedekind cut. Clearly $1 \in D$ and $2 \notin D$, so that (1) holds. Now let $a \in D$ and assume $b < a$ for $a, b \in Q_p$. Then $b < a$ implies that $b^2 < ab < a^2$ so that $b^2 < 2$. Hence $b \in D$ and (2) holds. Since $2 - a^2 > 0$, by Theorem 5.5.3 there exists a positive integer n such that $2 - a^2 > (2a + 1)/n$. Then

$$\begin{aligned} (a + 1/n)^2 &= a^2 + 2a/n + 1/n^2 \\ &\leq a^2 + (2a + 1)/n \\ &< 2. \end{aligned}$$

Hence $a + 1/n \in D$ and $a < a + 1/n$. Hence (3) holds. In the sequel we will want to associate this cut D with the "number" $\sqrt{2}$.

7.3.2 Definition. *Let S denote the set of all Dedekind cuts. For all $C, D \in S$, define*

$$C + D = \{c + d \mid c \in C, d \in D\}$$

and

$$C \cdot D = \{c \cdot d \mid c \in C, d \in D\}.$$

Furthermore for $C, D \in S$, set

$$C < D \quad \text{if} \quad C \subseteq D.$$

If $D \in S$ and $\tilde{D}$ denotes the complement of D in Q_p, set

$$D^{-1} = \{b \in Q_p \mid b < d^{-1} \text{ for some } d \in \tilde{D}\}.$$

*Then D^{-1} is called the **inverse** of D.*

It is not obvious that $C + D$, $C \cdot D$, and D^{-1} are cuts for all $C, D \in S$. We will prove that $C + D$ is a cut and leave the proof that $C \cdot D$ and D^{-1} are cuts as an exercise.

7.3.3 Theorem. *For all Dedekind cuts C and D, $C + D$, $C \cdot D$, and D^{-1} are also Dedekind cuts.*

Proof
1) Clearly $C + D \neq \emptyset$. Since $C \neq Q_p$ and $D \neq Q_p$, there exist $c, d \in Q_p$ such that $c \notin C, d \notin D$. Thus $c + d$ is greater than every element in $C + D$, so $c + d \notin C + D$. Thus $C + D \neq Q_p$.
2) Let $c + d \in C + D$ with $c \in C$, $d \in D$ and let $a \in Q_p$ be such that $a < c + d$. We must show that $a \in C + D$. Since $a < c + d$ we have $a/(c + d) < 1$. Thus $ac/(c + d) < c$ and hence $ac/(c + d) \in C$. Similarly $ad/(c + d) \in D$ and therefore $a = ac/(c + d) + ad/(c + d) \in C + D$.
3) Again, let $c + d \in C + D$ with $c \in C$, $d \in D$. Since D is a cut, there exists $d_1 \in D$ such that $d < d_1$. Then $c + d_1 \in C + D$ and $c + d < c + d_1$.

For the next theorem, recall that D_1 is the cut defined by

$$D_1 = \{x \in Q_p \mid x < 1\}.$$

7.3.4 Theorem.

1) *The operations $+$ and $\cdot$ defined on S are commutative, associative binary operations. Furthermore $\cdot$ is left- and right-distributive over $+$.*
2) *For all $D \in S$, $D \cdot D_1 = D$ and $D \cdot D^{-1} = D_1$.*
3) *The trichotomy law holds for $<$ on S.*

Proof. The proofs of (1) and (3) are straightforward and are left as exercises. We will prove that $D \cdot D^{-1} = D_1$ and leave $D \cdot D_1 = D$ as an exercise also.

Let $a \in D \cdot D^{-1}$; then $a = bc$ where $b \in D$, $c \in D^{-1}$. Since $c \in D^{-1}$, there exists $d \in \tilde{D}$ such that $c < d^{-1}$. Then $dc < 1$. Since $b \in D$ and $d \in \tilde{D}$, $b < d$. Hence $bc < dc < 1$; therefore $a < 1$ so that $a \in D_1$. This proves that $D \cdot D^{-1} \subseteq D_1$.

Now let $a \in D_1$; then $a < 1$ and $a^{-1} > 1$. We will show that for all $d \in D$, $d^{-1}a \in D^{-1}$ and so $a = d(d^{-1}a) \in D \cdot D^{-1}$, which will complete the proof. There exists a positive integer n such that $1/n \in D$. Let $b = (1 - a)/an$. If $b \in \tilde{D}$, then there exists $c \in D$ such that $b + c \in \tilde{D}$. If $b \in D$, then there exists a smallest positive integer k such that $kb \in \tilde{D}$. Then $k > 1$, $(k - 1)b \in D$, and $(k - 1)b + b \in \tilde{D}$. In this case, let $c = (k - 1)b$. Then in either case, $c \in D$ and $b + c \in \tilde{D}$. Moreover, since $1/n \in D$, we can pick c such that $c > 1/n$. Then

$$0 < (cn - 1)(1 - a)/an = ca^{-1} - b - c.$$

Hence $ca^{-1} \in \tilde{D}$. If d is any element of D, then $d > c$ and hence $d^{-1}a < c^{-1}a = (ca^{-1})^{-1}$. Hence, since $ca^{-1} \in \tilde{D}$, $d^{-1}a \in D^{-1}$. Thus, as claimed, $a = d(d^{-1}a) \in D \cdot D^{-1}$.

We now have the system of positive real numbers. If we carry out a construction on the positive real numbers as we did to obtain the system of integers from the natural numbers, we obtain the system of all *real numbers*, which we denote by R. Then $R_p = \{D \in R \mid D > 0\}$ is the set of positive elements which make R an ordered field.

It is easy to see, considering 7.3.9, Exercise 3, that the mapping $\alpha: Q \to R$ given by $\alpha(x) = D_x$ is an isomorphism which also preserves the ordering. Hence, as usual, we identify the elements of Q with their images under α in R. Consequently, $Q \subseteq R$, and when we speak of a rational number, we may as well assume that it is also a real number. Moreover, even though by our construction, the system of real numbers consists of Dedekind cuts, for which we have used capital letters as symbols, it is quite common to use lower case letters to denote elements of R. Hence, if we say "$x \in R$," x will be a Dedekind cut. Therefore x is a set of positive rational numbers, and as such has elements itself. Hence the term "rational number" is used in two ways simultaneously: (1) as a real number, i.e., as a Dedekind cut of the form D_x; and (2) as an element of a Dedekind cut.

We have seen that both the set of rational numbers and the set of real numbers are ordered fields. However, there is one important property which the set of real numbers enjoys that the set of rational numbers does not have. This property is *completeness*. We will prove that R is complete, but that Q is not. But first we need some definitions and a theorem.

7.3.5 Definition. *Let F be any nonempty subset of an ordered field. If there exists an element x such that $x \geq f$ for all $f \in F$, then x is called an* **upper bound of F.**

Let us consider some examples. Let R be the field of real numbers. Let $F = \{r \in R \mid r \leq 4\}$. Then 4 and any real number larger than 4 are upper bounds of F. Hence upper bounds are not unique. If $E = \{r \in R \mid r < 4\}$, then 4 and any real number larger than 4 are also upper bounds of E. Hence upper bounds need not belong to the set. On the other hand, not every set has an upper bound; for instance, the set of integers has no upper bound.

7.3.6 Definition. *Let F be a nonempty subset of an ordered field. If the set of upper bounds of F has a least element y in it, then y is said to be the* **least upper bound of F.**

In both the sets E and F discussed above, 4 is the least upper bound. Notice that the least upper bound need not belong to the set. We have seen that a set may not have any upper bounds. However, if a set of *real numbers* has an upper bound, then it has a least upper bound. This property is called the *completeness property*. A system with the completeness property is said to be *complete*.

Before proving that R is complete, we will state and prove an important theorem due to Dedekind.

7.3.7 Theorem (Dedekind). *Let U be a set of real numbers satisfying the following conditions.*

1) *U contains a positive rational number and $U \neq R$.*

2) *If $x \in U$ and $y < x$, then $y \in U$.*

Then there exists a unique real number z such that $u < z$ implies $u \in U$ and $z < v$ implies $v \notin U$. Conditions (1) and (2) are known as the **Dedekind Conditions.**

Proof. First we will show the uniqueness of z. Suppose there are two distinct elements z_1, z_2 satisfying the conclusion of the theorem. Then, without loss of generality, we may assume that $z_1 < z_2$. Hence, by 7.3.9, Exercise 7, there exists a rational number a such that $z_1 < a < z_2$. From $z_1 < a$, we see that $a \notin U$. On the other hand, from $a < z_2$, $a \in U$. This contradiction establishes the uniqueness of z.

Now we prove the existence of z. Define

$$Z = \{b \in Q_p \mid b \in x \text{ for some real number } x \in U\}.$$

First we will show that Z is a Dedekind cut.

1) Since U contains a positive real number, Z is not empty. Let y be a real number not in U, and let c be a positive rational number not in y. Then $c \notin Z$, for, if $c \in Z$, then $c \in x$ for some real number $x \in U$. But $x < y$, a contradiction.

2) Let a be an arbitrary element of Q_p such that $a < b$ for some $b \in Z$. Since $b \in x$ for some $x \in U$, then $a < b$ implies that $a \in x$. Hence $a \in Z$.

3) Let $b \in Z$. Then there exists a real number $x \in U$ such that $b \in x$. Then there exists $c \in x$ such that $b < c$. Hence Z is a Dedekind cut. We will use the lower case z in place of Z for the remainder of the proof.

Now we must show that z satisfies the conclusion of the theorem. Suppose $u < z$. Then there exists $a \in Q_p$ such that $a \notin u$, $a \in z$. But since $a \in z$, $a \in x$ for some $x \in U$. The facts $a \notin u$ and $a \in x$ imply that $u < x$. Hence, since $x \in U$, (2) implies that $u \in U$. On the other hand, suppose $z < v$. Then there exists $c \in Q_p$ such that $c \notin z$, $c \in v$. If $v \in U$, then $c \in z$ contrary to our choice of c. Hence $v \notin U$. This proves the theorem.

Condition (1) may be relaxed to require only that U contain a real number and $U \neq R$ by realizing that every real number contains a rational number and, in case U contains no positive rationals, by using the construction of R R from S to obtain the result.

Now we are ready for the theorem for which we have been preparing.

7.3.8 Theorem (Completeness Property). *The system R of real numbers is complete; i.e., every nonempty subset of R which has an upper bound has a least upper bound.*

Proof. Let U be a nonempty subset of R which has an upper bound. We will determine the least upper bound of U. Define a subset of R by

$$V = \{x \in R \mid \text{there exists } u \in U \text{ such that } u > x\}.$$

Next we prove that V satisfies the Dedekind Conditions.

1) Since U is not empty, there exists a real number $u \in U$. Then every real number less than u belongs to V, so V is not empty. Also, since U has an upper bound, say y, there exist real numbers larger than y which are not elements of V. Thus $V \neq R$.

2) Let $x \in V$ and suppose $y < x$. Since $x \in V$, there exists $u \in U$ such that $x < u$. Then $y < u$, so that $y \in V$.

Hence, by Theorem 7.3.7, there exists a unique real number z such that $u < z$ implies $u \in V$ and $z < v$ implies that $v \notin V$. We will prove that z is the least upper bound of U. First we prove that z is an upper bound of U and then that z is the *least* upper bound. Suppose z is not an upper bound of U. Then there exists $r \in U$ such that $z < r$. Let s be a real number such that $z < s < r$. Since $s < r$, then $s \in V$, by definition of V; but $z < s$ implies that $s \notin V$. This contradiction implies that z is an upper bound of U. Furthermore, for every positive real number t, $z - t < z$. Hence, for every positive real number t, $z - t \in V$. Thus $z - t < u$ for some $u \in U$. Thus no real numbers less than z are upper bounds of U. Hence z is the least upper bound of U.

To show that the system Q of rational numbers is not complete, we will show that the nonempty subset $A = \{x \in Q_p \mid x^2 < 2\}$ which has an upper bound does not have a least upper bound. Clearly A is not empty and does have an upper bound. Suppose A does have a least upper bound in Q; call it z. Then $z^2 \in Q$ and, by the trichotomy law, exactly one of the following is true: $z^2 = 2$, $z^2 < 2$, or $z^2 > 2$. But there is no rational number such that $z^2 = 2$, so $z^2 < 2$ or $z^2 > 2$. We will show that these two possibilities lead to contradictions, and therefore we will prove that A has no least upper bound in Q.

If $z^2 < 2$, then one can show that if $x = 4z/(z^2 + 2)$, then $z < x$ and $x^2 < 2$, contradicting the fact that z is the least upper bound of A. On the other hand, if $z^2 > 2$, then if $y = (z^2 + 2)/2z$, then $y < z$ and y is an upper bound of a, again contradicting our choice of z. This completes the proof.

7.3.9 Exercises

1. Prove in detail that for each $a \in Q_p$, D_a is a Dedekind cut.
2. Prove that $C \cdot D$ and D^{-1} are cuts for all $C, D \in S$.
3. Let $x, y \in Q_p$. Prove the following.
   a) $D_x + D_y = D_{x+y}$
   b) $D_x \cdot D_y = D_{xy}$
   c) $D_x < D_y$ if and only if $x < y$
4. Prove parts (1) and (3) of Theorem 7.3.4.
5. Prove that $D \cdot D_1 = D$ for all $D \in S$.
6. Carry out the details of constructing R from S.
7. Let C and D be arbitrary real numbers such that $C < D$. Prove that there exists a rational number a such that
$$C < D_a < D.$$
8. Fill in all details of the discussion which proves that Q is not complete.

7.4 THE COMPLEX NUMBERS

The construction of the system C of complex numbers from the system of real numbers is relatively simple. In this section we sketch the construction and leave the proofs as exercises. Throughout the section we will use lower case letters to represent elements of R.

From our experience in college algebra, we know that complex numbers are "numbers" of the form $a + bi$ where $i^2 = -1$. However, we cannot assume that such a number i exists. We avoid this by considering ordered pairs (a, b) of real numbers. However, one may intuitively think of (a, b) as $a + bi$; this will motivate the definitions we will give.

7.4.1 Definition. *Let C be the set of all ordered pairs (a, b) of real numbers. Define $+$ and $\cdot$ on C by*

$$(a, b) + (c, d) = (a + c, b + d)$$

and

$$(a, b) \cdot (c, d) = (ac - bd, ad + bc)$$

for all (a, b), $(c, d) \in C$.

7.4.2 Theorem. *Then C is a field with the binary operations defined above; and C contains a subfield $\{(a, 0) \mid a \in R\}$ which is isomorphic to R.*

The proof that C is a field is simply a matter of verifying that the axioms for a field are satisfied. The isomorphism between R and $\{(a, 0) \mid a \in R\}$ is obvious. The details are left as an exercise. The field C is called the field of *complex numbers.*

Note that any complex number (a, b) can be written in the following form:

$$(a, b) = (a, 0) + (b, 0) \cdot (0, 1).$$

Under the isomorphism between R and $\{(a, 0) \mid a \in R\}$, we can identify $a \in R$ with $(a, 0) \in C$. Also we denote the complex number $(0, 1)$ by i. Then every complex number (a, b) can be expressed as $a + bi$ and $i^2 = -1$.

It is important to observe that C is not an ordered field, for if C were ordered, then, by Theorem 5.4.3, $a^2 > 0$ for all nonzero $a \in C$. But $i \in C$, $i \neq 0$, and $i^2 < 0$.

In this chapter we have progressed through a series of constructions which have netted us the usual number systems: the natural numbers N, the integers I, the rational numbers Q, the real numbers R, and the complex numbers C. Furthermore, by identifying elements with their images under the appropriate isomorphisms, we have the following inclusion relations between these systems:

$$N \subseteq I \subseteq Q \subseteq R \subseteq C.$$

Notice that at first, as we increase the set of elements in the systems, the systems gain important properties. For instance, N is not even a ring, whereas I is an ordered integral domain. By constructing Q from I, we gain multiplicative inverses and hence a field. The completeness property is a property that R enjoys but Q does not. Hence each new construction produced a system which had a property its predecessor did not have. However, in constructing C from R, we lose all the ordering properties since C is not an ordered field. Heuristically this phenomenon may be explained in the following. By increasing the algebraic properties of the number system C, we have destroyed the ordering properties.

7.4.3 Exercises

1. Prove that C is a field with the binary operations defined in 7.4.1.

2. Prove that C contains a subfield isomorphic to R.

3. What would be wrong with defining the multiplication on c by $(a, b) \cdot (c, d) = (ac, bd)$?

ADDITIONAL REFERENCES FOR CHAPTER 7

BARTLE, ROBERT G., *The Elements of Real Analysis*, New York: John Wiley and Sons (1964).

CROUCH, RALPH and ELBERT WALKER, *Introduction to Modern Algebra and Analysis*, New York: Holt, Rinehart, and Winston (1962).

DEDEKIND, RICHARD, *Essays on the Theory of Numbers*, New York: Dover Publications (1963).

McCOY, NEAL H., *Introduction to Modern Algebra*, Boston: Allyn and Bacon (1962).

RIBENBOIM, PAULO, *Functions, Limits, and Continuity*, New York: John Wiley and Sons (1964).

RUDIN, WALTER, *Principles of Mathematical Analysis*, second edition, New York: McGraw-Hill (1964).

THURSTON, H. A., *The Number-System*, New York: Interscience (1956).

YOUSE, BEVAN K., *The Number System*, Belmont, California: Dickenson Publishing Company (1965).

INDEX

INDEX

A

Abel, Niels Henrik, 25
Abelian group, 25
Absolute value, 99
Addition, of complex numbers, 134
  of continuous functions, 66
  of integers, 126
  of matrices, 32, 63
  of natural numbers, 124
  of polynomials, 105
  of rational numbers, 94
  of real numbers, 130
Additive group of a ring, 58, 90
Additive identity, 57
Additive inverse, 57
Archimedian Property, 101
Associates, 79
Associative law, 19, 24, 57
  generalized, 68

B

Biconditional, 12
Binary operation, 19

C

Cancellation law, 27
  of multiplication, 89
Canonical epimorphism, 56
Cantor, Georg, 129
Cartesian product, 3
  generalized, 3
Cauchy, Augustin, 129
Closure property, 19, 24
Coefficient of a polynomial, 104
Commutative law, 19, 57
  generalized, 68, 69
Commutative ring, 59

Complement, 3, 15
Completeness property, 133
Complex numbers, system of, 134
Composition of mappings, 6
Conditional, 11, 13
Congruence, modulo H, 44
  modulo n, 17, 31, 62
  modulo $f(x)$, 120
Conjunction, 10
Constant term of a polynomial, 109
Construction, of the complex
    numbers, 135
  of the field of quotients, 92
  of the integers, 126
  of the natural numbers, 124
  of the rational numbers, 94, 128
  of the real numbers, 129
Contrapositive, 13
Coset, 43
Cut, 129
Cyclic group, 40

D

Dedekind, Richard, 129
Dedekind Conditions, 132
Dedekind cut, 129
Degree of a polynomial, 109
De Morgan, Augustus, 13
De Morgan's Laws, 13
Disjoint sets, 2
Disjunction, 11
  exclusive, 11
Distributive laws, 19, 57
  generalized, 69
Divides, 21, 77, 111
Division Algorithm, 21, 78, 112
Division ring, 58
Divisor, 21, 77, 111

E

Eisenstein, F. M. G., 119
Eisensteins's Criterion, 119
Embedded, 95
Empty set, 1
Epimorphism, canonical, 56
    of groups, 54
    of rings, 74
Equality, of mappings, 4
    of matrices, 32, 63
    of polynomials, 105
    of sets, 1
Equivalence of propositions, 12
Equivalence relation, 16
Equivalence classes, 16
Euclidean Algorithm, 82, 116
Exponents, 29

F

Factor, 77, 111
Factor group, 50
Factor Theorem, 113
Field, 89
    of complex numbers, 135
    of quotients, 92
    of rational numbers, 94, 128
    of real numbers, 129
Finite group, 29
Function, 4
Fundamental Theorem of Arithmetic, 86
Fundamental Theorem of Homomorphisms, 56

G

Galois, Evariste, 48
Gauss, Carl Friedrich, 118
Gauss' Lemma, 118

Generalized associative law, 68
Generalized Cartesian product, 3
Generalized commutative law, 68, 69
Generalized distributive law, 69
Generalized intersection, 2
Generalized product, 68
Generalized sum, 68
Generalized union, 2
Generator of a group, 40
Greatest common divisor, of integers, 80
    of polynomials, 115
Group, 24
    abelian, 25
    cyclic, 40
    factor, 50
    finite, 29
    infinite, 29
    of permutations, 33
    of rotations of a square, 35
    symmetric, 33

H

Homomorphism, of groups, 52
    of rings, 73

I

Ideal, 70
    principal, 71
Identity, additive, 57
    of a group, 24
    mapping, 5
    multiplicative, 57
Image under a mapping, 4, 53, 74
Indeterminate, 103
Index, 46
Indirect proof, 14
Induction, 22, 124

Inductive definition, 22, 29
Infinite group, 29
Infinite set, 9
Integers, 126
    modulo n, 31, 62, 91
Integral domain, 88
Intersection, 2
    generalized, 2
Inverse, additive, 57
    of a cut, 130
    of an element, 24, 28
    of a mapping, 8
    multiplicative, 58
Irreducible polynomial, 111
Isomorphism, of groups, 54
    of rings, 74

K

Kernel, of a group homomorphism, 53
    of a ring homomorphism, 74

L

Lagrange, Joseph Louis, 45
Lagrange's Theorem, 45
Laws of exponents, 29
Leading coefficient, 109
Least common multiple, 84
Least element, 125
Least upper bound, 132
Left coset, 43
Linear combination, of integers, 81
    of polynomials, 116
Logically equivalent, 12

M

Mapping, 4
    composition of, 6
    identity, 5

    one-to-one, 6
    onto, 6
Mathematical induction, 22
    strong form, 23
Matrix, 32
    addition of, 32, 63
    equality of, 32, 63
    multiplication of, 63
Modulo n, 17, 31, 62
Modulo $f(x)$, 120
Monic polynomial, 111
Monomorphism, of groups, 54
    of rings, 74
Multiple, 77, 111
Multiplication, of complex number,
        134
    of continuous functions, 66
    of integers, 126
    of matrices, 63
    of natural numbers, 124
    of polynomials, 105
    of rational numbers, 94
    of real numbers, 130
Multiplicative group of a field, 90
Multiplicative inverse, 58

N

Natural numbers, 123
Negative elements, 98
Negation, 10
Normal subgroup, 47
Normalizer of a subgroup, 52
Not, 10
Null set, 1

O

One-to-one mapping, 6
Onto mapping, 6

Order, of a group, 29
  of a group element, 41
Ordered field, 98
Ordered integral domain, 97
Ordering, 97

P

Partition, 3, 18
Peano, Giuseppe, 124
Peano's Postulates, 124
Permutation, 33
Polynomials, 103
Positive elements, 98
Prime integer, 77
Prime polynomial, 111
Primitive polynomial, 118
Principal ideal, 71
Proper subset, 1
Proposition, 10

Q

Quantifiers, 13
Quotient, 79, 112
Quotient field of an integral domain, 92

R

Rational numbers, 37
Real numbers, 128
Recursive definition, 22, 29
Reduced form, 100
Reflexive property of a relation, 16
Relation, 16
  equivalence, 16
  reflexive, 16
  symmetric, 16
  transitive, 16

Relatively prime integers, 81
Remainder, 79, 112
Remainder Theorem, 113
Ring, 57
  of all subsets of a set, 65
  of continuous functions, 65
  of integers modulo n, 62
  of matrices, 63
  of polynomials, 106
  of polynomials modulo $f(x)$, 120
  with unity element, 58
Root of a polynomial, 113
Rotations of a square, 35

S

Set, 1
Standard form of an integer, 87
Subgroup, 38
  cyclic, 40
  normal, 47
Subring, 70
Subset, 1
Successor, 124
Symmetric group, 33
Symmetric property of a relation, 16

T

Term of a polynomial, 104
Transitive property of a relation, 16
Trichotomy law, 98

U

Union, 2
  generalized, 2
Unique factorization,
  of integers, 86
  of polynomials, 117

Uniqueness, 14
   of group identity, 27
   of inverse, 59
   of unity element, 59
Unit, 92
Unity element, 58
Upper bound, 131

W

Well-defined operation, 4, 19, 31, 49
Well-ordered set, 125

Z

Zero divisor, 88
Zero of a ring, 58

ABCDE698